SING IN

A SONGBOOK FOR CHRISTIAN YOUTH

COMPILED BY:

WARREN G. STITT
FRED BOCK

PRODUCTION DESIGN BY:
R. PAUL FIRNHABER

A Charles Hansen Publication

in conjunction with

Sacred Songs

INTRODUCTION

Young people love to sing. Through singing they share common feelings and experiences. When a man of faith is troubled, he sings his sorrows. When he is happy, he often finds a song is the best way to express his joy. Songs are for every season, good and bad.

In this fast-moving, electronic age, man needs music more than ever. There's more to be troubled about and more to be happy about. Knowledge is doubling every decade, our population is increasing by giant proportions, and now we're reaching beyond our world to outer space. Our lives are so full and complicated it becomes more difficult to express our convictions of faith, to link what we believe with how we live. Young people, particularly, need new songs for these "new" seasons. They need songs that speak to the unusual as well as the usual, to the complex as well as the simple, to the changing as well as the unchanging. While our Christian faith is relevant to this age as it has been to every age, our expressions of faith—our songs, for instance—have not always kept up with the times.

That's why we're glad to introduce "Sing In." We feel it provides what singing Christians need today—a good cross-section of old and new songs that young people would want to sing and learn, presented in a way that would provide a creative link between their faith and their fast-paced lives. "Sing In" is the brainchild of Success With Youth, one of the largest independent publishers of Christian youth material. I responded enthusiastically when they told me of their idea for this unique song book for Christian teens.

I'm sure you'll agree "Sing In" is refreshingly different. A quick glance at the song titles reveals a fine selection of hymns and familiar gospel songs. These are augmented by fresh new tunes and lyrics from the creative pens of contemporary Christian songwriters. Finally, we rounded out the book with selections of fun songs, camp songs, pop and folk tunes, to provide a healthy balance and to insure suitability for nearly any occasion.

One further note. One of the most unique aspects of "Sing In" is the illustrations that accompany the songs. Many are ad slogans from magazines and television commercials—words and sayings familiar to everyone today. Surprisingly, when linked to Christian songs, they suggest new and deeper meanings for both the headlines and the songs they illustrate. Each one has been carefully chosen. We want them to make you think about what the songs have to say and what life is all about. Spend time with them. Talk about them. Let them broaden your Christian experience.

And finally, a few acknowledgments are in order. Few people realize what it takes to put a songbook together. This book, for example, has been a year in the making. Russ Reid, of Success With Youth, spawned the idea. Warren Stitt devoted months of time to make it all happen. Fred Bock handled the mass of details such as copyright permissions and mechanical uniformity. And Paul Firnhaber interpreted the songs with a unique artistic treatment. I'm grateful to each of them as I know you will be as you enjoy this book. We hope "Sing In" will help you live your faith more meaningfully.

Jarrell McCracken, President
Word, Inc.

1 BE KIND TRYIN'

R. H. Ray Hildebrand

Guitar (Vamp)
D
G
Dbass
VERSE: What has happened to... all these kids today, What has happened to... our present gene-
(Spoken ration and their aspiration... They don't appreciate... a single thing any more... What
Freely) they can't buy, they can steal or... stomp on the floor or... slam the door.........
D
A7
1. One lit-tle pill what a thrill, Who cares if ya pass on a hill
2. Too much "Let's take a drink," "Let's get more mon-ey in the
D
A7
bank," Too much have a good time, And
Too much gone all the time,
G
D
G
D
Fine
not e-nough be kind try-in' Not e-nough be kind try-in'.
Guitar (Vamp)
D. S. al Fine
Well Here's my answer to that, (Bein' a kid.)... What has happened to... Mom and Dad today....
(Spoken What has happend to... that Love and respect, and that old hug around the neck... They don't
Freely) have much time for kids any more.... It's, "Go out and play" or... "You're in the way;"... Not "I
love ya honey," but "Here, take some money!"

If we tell you something about yourself, promise you won't get mad?

2 HE'S EVERYTHING TO ME

R. C. Ralph Carmichael

Accented
mf
In the stars His hand-i - work I see, On the wind He speaks with maj - es-ty, Though He rul-eth o-ver land and sea, what is that to me?
I will cel - e-brate Na-ti - vi-ty, For it has a place in his - to-ry,
Sure, He came to set His peo - ple free, what is that to me?

Why take less?

Today's reason why...

Does it seem too good to be true?

3 SURELY GOODNESS AND MERCY

J. W. P. & A. B. S. — John W. Peterson & Alfred B. Smith

F Bb Gm
A pil - grim was I and a wan - d'ring, In the
He re - stor - eth my soul when I'm wea - ry He
C7 F
cold night of sin I did roam; When
giv - eth me strength day by day. He
Bb Gm
Je - sus the kind Shep - herd found me, And
leads me be - side the still wa - ters, He
F C7 F
now I am on my way home.
guards me each step of the way.
F
Sure - ly good - ness and mer - cy shall
C7
fol - low me all the days, all the
F
days of my life. Sure - ly
good - ness and mer - cy shall fol - low

Guaranteed won't wear out!

Come and find out what kind of stuff you're made of.

4 BORN FREE

D. B. & J. B.

Don Black and John Barry

5 JUST A CLOSER WALK WITH THEE

Traditional

1. I am weak but Thou art strong, Je - sus keeps me from all wrong,
2. Through this world of toils and snares, If I fal - ter Lord who cares,
3. When my fee - ble life is o'er, Times for me won't be no more,
I'll be sat - is - fied as long, As I walk, Let me walk, close with Thee.
Who with me my bur-den shares, None but Thee, dear Lord, none but Thee.
Guide me gent-ly, safe-ly o'er To Thy king - dom shore, to Thy shore.
REFRAIN
Just a clos - er walk with Thee; Grant it Je - sus if you please,
rit.
Dai - ly walk - ing close with Thee, Let it be, dear Lord, let it be.

make your move

Call the mover who can make it look easy.

6 A MIGHTY FORTRESS IS OUR GOD

M. L. Martin Luther

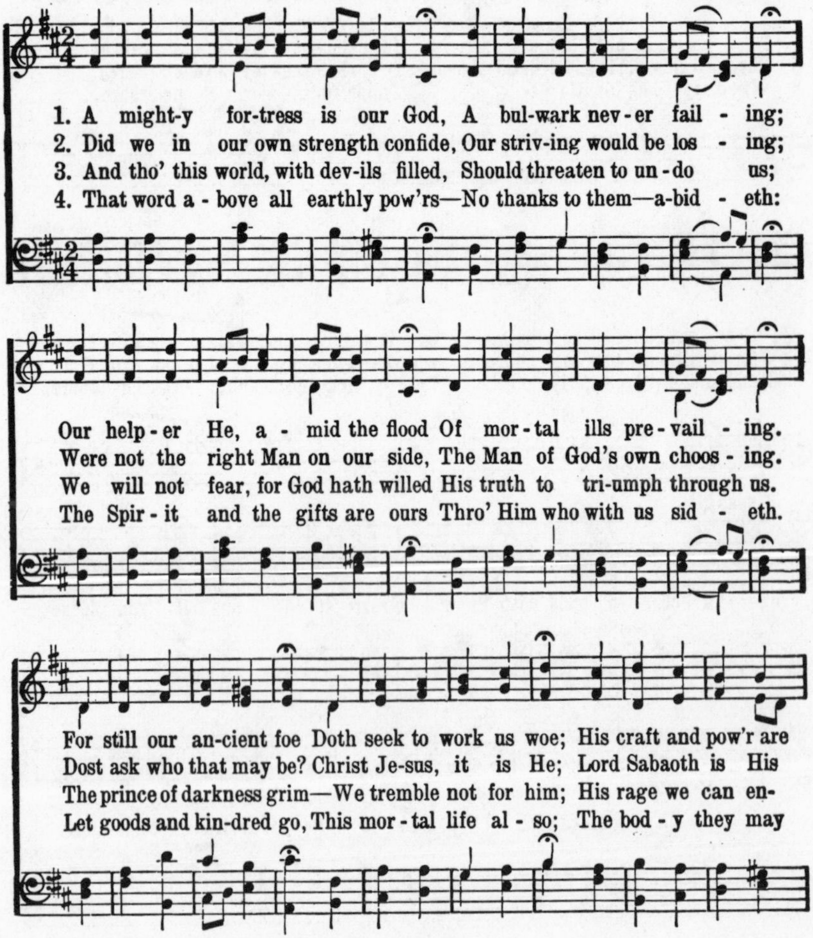
1. A might-y for-tress is our God, A bul-wark nev-er fail - ing;
2. Did we in our own strength confide, Our striv-ing would be los - ing;
3. And tho' this world, with dev-ils filled, Should threaten to un-do us;
4. That word a - bove all earthly pow'rs—No thanks to them—a-bid - eth:
Our help-er He, a - mid the flood Of mor-tal ills pre-vail - ing.
Were not the right Man on our side, The Man of God's own choos - ing.
We will not fear, for God hath willed His truth to tri-umph through us.
The Spir-it and the gifts are ours Thro' Him who with us sid - eth.
For still our an-cient foe Doth seek to work us woe; His craft and pow'r are
Dost ask who that may be? Christ Je-sus, it is He; Lord Sabaoth is His
The prince of darkness grim—We tremble not for him; His rage we can en-
Let goods and kin-dred go, This mor-tal life al - so; The bod - y they may

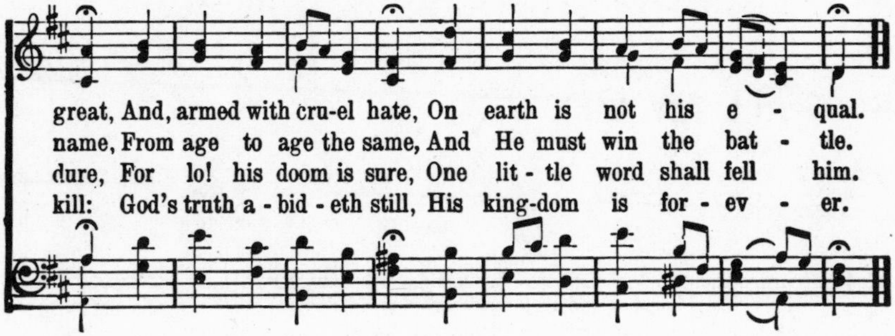
great, And, armed with cru-el hate, On earth is not his e - qual.
name, From age to age the same, And He must win the bat - tle.
dure, For lo! his doom is sure, One lit - tle word shall fell him.
kill: God's truth a - bid - eth still, His king-dom is for - ev - er.

7 KUM BA YA

Traditional

C F C C F
Kum ba yah, my Lord, Kum ba yah! Kum ba yah, my Lord, Kum ba
G C F C F C G7 C
yah! Kum ba yah, my Lord, Kum ba yah! O Lord, Kum ba yah.

Pronounced: "Koom-bah-yah."

Someone's crying, Lord Kum ba yah!
Someone's singing, Lord Kum ba yah!
Someone's praying, Lord Kum ba yah!

Quick

overgive.

8 ALL MY LIFE

R. C. — Ralph Carmichael

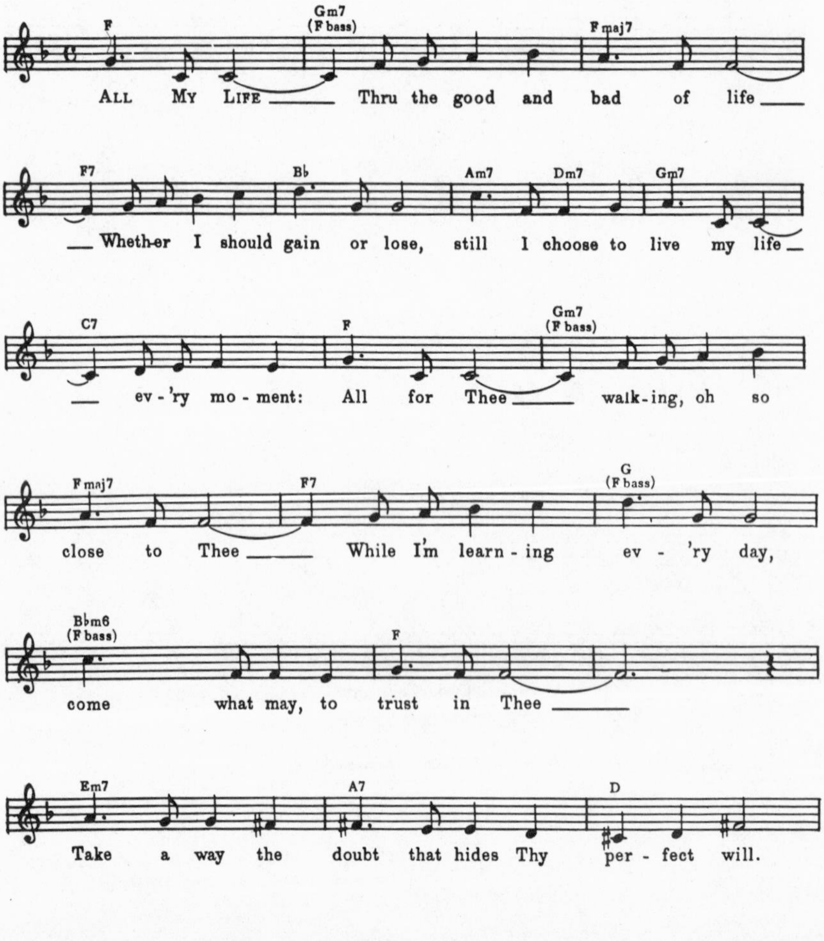
ALL MY LIFE ___ Thru the good and bad of life ___
___ Whether I should gain or lose, still I choose to live my life ___
___ ev-'ry mo-ment: All for Thee ___ walk-ing, oh so
close to Thee ___ While I'm learn-ing ev-'ry day,
come what may, to trust in Thee ___
Take a way the doubt that hides Thy per-fect will.

Dm7 G7
Give me faith, in - stead, and with Thy
Gm C7♭9 F Gm7 (F bass)
spir - it fill. Then all my days, be the guard - ian
Fmaj7 F7 G (F bass)
of my ways, and I'll know the glo - ry of
B♭m6 (F bass) 1 F
all Thy love thru all my days
2
all my days.

What are Good Guys made of?

Why take less?

9 IF YOU KNOW THE LORD

B. R.

Bickley Reichner

With feeling - not fast
If you know the Lord, You need no - bo - dy else To see you through
the dark-est night. You can walk a - lone, You on-ly need the
Lord, He'll keep you on the road marked right. Take time to
pray ev - 'ry day, And when you're head-in' home He'll
3
show you the way. If you know the Lord, You need no - bo - dy

else, to see the light, His won-der-ful light.

10 ALL THINGS THROUGH CHRIST

H. W. G. Homer W. Grimes

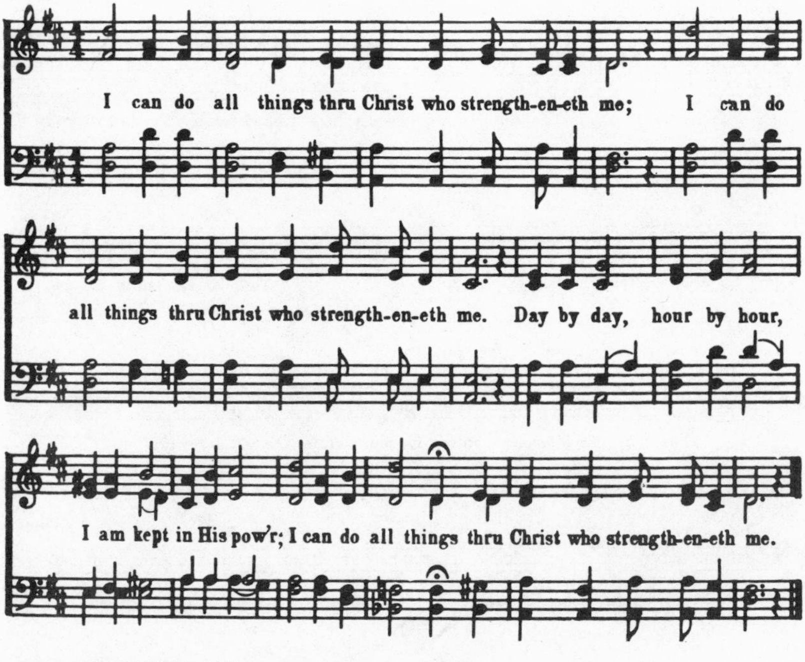
I can do all things thru Christ who strength-en-eth me; I can do
all things thru Christ who strength-en-eth me. Day by day, hour by hour,
I am kept in His pow'r; I can do all things thru Christ who strength-en-eth me.

promises in the world.

the

11 YESTERDAY, TODAY & TOMORROW

Jack Wyrtzen

Don Wyrtzen

G A7 D F#m G A9 D Bm Em A
comes for me. He comes, To-mor-row He comes for me, comes for me.
D Bm G D Bb Eb Cm Fm Bb Eb Cm
This is my-ste-ry. Oh, friend, do you know Him. Know Him,
Fm Bb7 Eb Gm Ab Bb7 Eb Gm Ab Bb9
Know Him, Oh, friend, do you know Him. Know Him, Oh, friend, do
Eb Cm Fm Bb Eb Cm Ab Eb
you know Him, Do you know Him. Je - sus Christ, the Lord.
Eb Cm Ab Eb Eb Cm Ab Eb
Je - sus Christ, the Lord. Je - sus Christ, the Lord.

This means more than all

There's a lot more than meets the eye.

12 HAVE YOU MET JESUS?

W. G. William Gillam

Have you met Je - sus, ___ my Lord and my
When you meet Je - sus ___ in all of His
When you crown Je - sus ___ your Lord and your
MAS TER? ___ Have you met Je - sus, ___ our won - der - ful
glo - ry ___ When face to face you ___ look full up - on
Mas - ter, ___ When on the throne of ___ your heart He doth
KING? ___ Your long - ing heart He ___ will fill to o'er-
Him ___ Earth's fair - est trea - sure ___ com - pared to His
reign ___ In sweet do - min - ion ___ He'll rule ab - so -
flow - ing ___ with sweet sat - is - fact - ion ___ and cause it to
won - der ___ will seem scarce - ly tin - sel ___ half glitt-'ring and
lute - ly ___ your will and your pas - sions ___ be - fore un - re-

sing! Have you tried Je - sus for life's great-est
dim When by God's Spir - it you come to know
strained And then that clean - ness of heart you had
prob - lem, the full re - demp - tion from bond-age to
JE - SUS, re - vealed com - plete - ly to your blind - ed
longed for A sense of pure - ness of ho - li - ness
sin? You'll nev er re - gret that you o-pened your
eyes, Your soul all - ex - ult - ant will shout hal - le -
true will sud-den-ly come to your soul ful - ly
heart's door in glad-some sur-rend-er and let Him come in.
lu - jah, at hav-ing met JE - SUS the King of the skies!
yield - ed a hap-py ful-fill - ment of God's will in you.

See him and be sure.

"I've got a headache?"

13 STANDIN' IN THE NEED OF PRAYER

Traditional Negro Spiritual

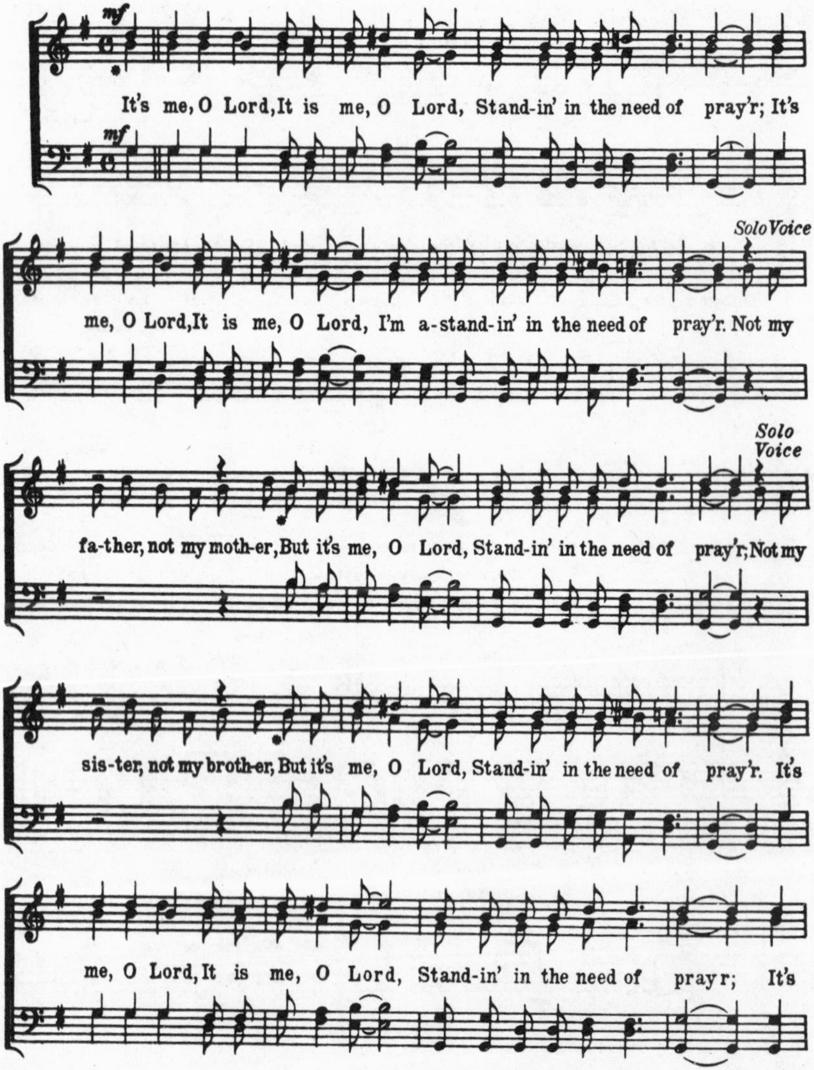
mf
It's me, O Lord, It is me, O Lord, Stand-in' in the need of pray'r; It's
mf
Solo Voice
me, O Lord, It is me, O Lord, I'm a-stand-in' in the need of pray'r. Not my
Solo Voice
fa-ther, not my moth-er, But it's me, O Lord, Stand-in' in the need of pray'r; Not my
sis-ter, not my broth-er, But it's me, O Lord, Stand-in' in the need of pray'r. It's
me, O Lord, It is me, O Lord, Stand-in' in the need of pray r; It's

"Take some aspirin."

*Melody

14 I HAVE DECIDED TO FOLLOW JESUS

An Indian Prince

Arr. by Norman Johnson

"I did. But it still hurts."

15 THE MAN

R. C. — Ralph Carmichael

Easy Folk Tempo
F
There once was a man, a long time a - go, A-stand-in' all a-lone a-gainst the
(But) some did-n't like Him 'twas plain to — see, 'Cause He — put 'em down for their hy-
F7
Bb7
stat - us quo. — He worked with His hands, and grew tall and strong, He
poc - ri - - cy. — The i - dea of lovin', was dras - tic and new, and
F
Am
worked with His mind a-sort-in' right from wrong. He was sure of His mis-sion and He
buck - in' the crowd was just — too much to do; — We ll — things have-n't changed from —
Bb
1 Gm7
C7
F
Bb7
spoke loud and clear, He got ev-'ry eye and He got — ev - 'ry —
those days of old, they
F
2 Gm7
C7
ear. — But still try to make Him — fit in-to their
F
Bb7
F
mold, fit in-to their mold. —
Bb7
F
— There is-n't a man or a wo-man too low, But

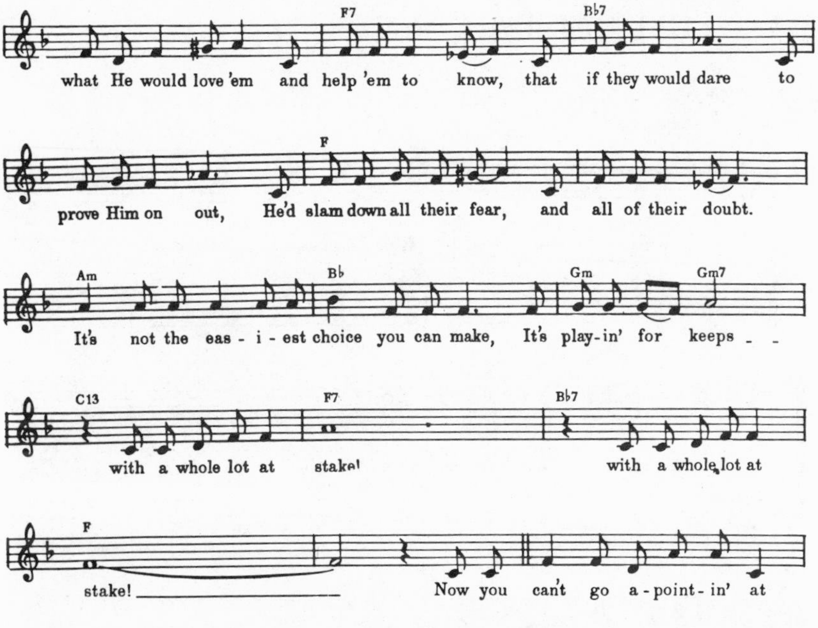
F7 Bb7
what He would love 'em and help 'em to know, that if they would dare to
F
prove Him on out, He'd slam down all their fear, and all of their doubt.
Am Bb Gm Gm7
It's not the eas - i - est choice you can make, It's play-in' for keeps
C13 F7 Bb7
with a whole lot at stake! with a whole lot at
F
stake!
Now you can't go a - point - in' at
what oth-ers do, 'Cause it's a per-son-al thing, strict-ly 'tween Him and you. And
Bb7 F
if you're real-ly want-in' to give life a pull, a - live to your fing-er tips,
Am Bb
brim-min' and full. Then give Him a try go-in' out on a limb, You'll
Gm C7 F Bb7 F
nev- er know life 'til you real-ly know Him.

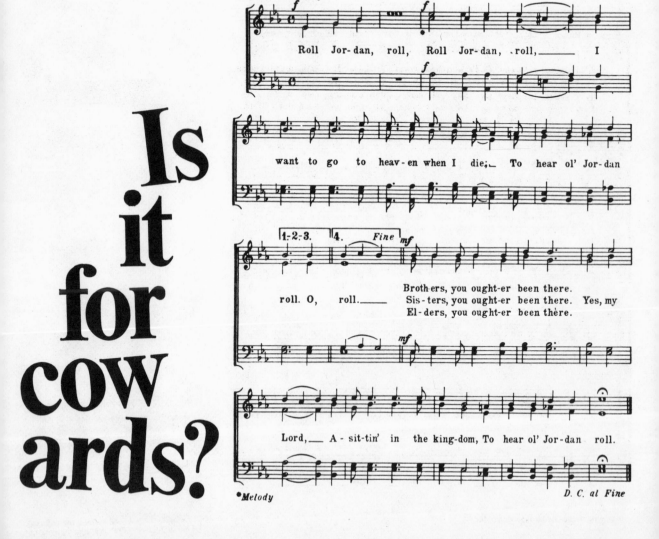

Is it for cowards?

16 ROLL, JORDAN, ROLL

Traditional Negro Spiritual

17 I KNOW WHOM I HAVE BELIEVED

Daniel W. Whittle

James McGranahan

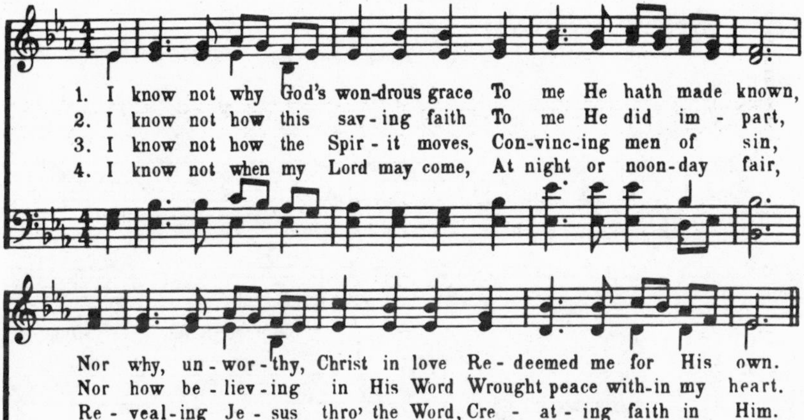
1. I know not why God's won-drous grace To me He hath made known,
2. I know not how this sav-ing faith To me He did im-part,
3. I know not how the Spir-it moves, Con-vinc-ing men of sin,
4. I know not when my Lord may come, At night or noon-day fair,
Nor why, un-wor-thy, Christ in love Re-deemed me for His own.
Nor how be-liev-ing in His Word Wrought peace with-in my heart.
Re-veal-ing Je-sus thro' the Word, Cre-at-ing faith in Him.
Nor if I'll walk the vale with Him, Or "meet Him in the air."
CHORUS
But "I know whom I have be-liev-ed, And am per-suad-ed that He is
a-ble To keep that which I've com-mit-ted Un-to Him a-gainst that day."

Finally?

18 SHENANDOAH

Traditional

O, Shenandoah, I love your daughter,
Away, you rolling river —
O, Shenandoah, I love your daughter,
Away, we're bound away, 'cross
the wide Missouri.

O, Shenandoah, I long to see you,
Away, you rolling river —
O, Shenandoah, I'll not deceive you,
Away, we're bound away, 'cross
the wide Missouri.

O, seven years, I've been a rover,
Away, you rolling river —
For seven years I've been a rover,
Away, we're bound away, 'cross
the wide Missouri.

19 GET TO DOIN'

R. H. — Ray Hildebrand

G C D7 Bm F
1. Down the road there's a man - sion tall, In - side lives a might - y rich man. He owns ev - 'ry - thing in our town, To - day they found a note in his hand and it read
2. Here he comes, his gui - tar in his hand, He trav - els all o - ver the place. He's got a name, all the girls play his game, But I've nev - er seen a smile on his face.
CHORUS
It's not mon - ey, no, no It's not suc - cess It's not for - tune or fame Here's what it is, He wrote it down Get To Do - in' what you're hap - py do - in'
Stop do - in' what you hate to do,
Life's too short to hate your way thru.
Get To Do - in' what you're hap - py do - in', and this ol' world will mean more to you. this ol' world will mean more to you.

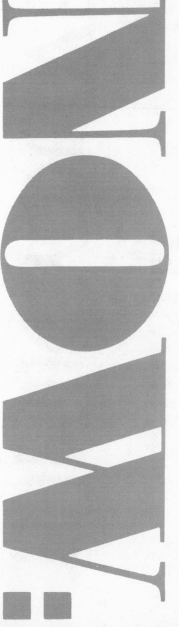

20 ONE OF THESE DAYS

R. C. Ralph Carmichael

Intro.
mf
G Em Cmaj7 C G Am7 D7
1. I looked a - bout one morn-ing and thru a mist-y sky I
2. I know the world is reel - ing, there's trou-ble ev-'ry-where. My
3. I may not live in com-fort but this I sure-ly know; I'll
G C G Em A7 D7
gazed up - on a bat-tle-field, man - kind was pass - ing by. I
heart goes out to ev-'ry-one be - set by fear and care. For
be con-tent with what I have while wait-ing here be - low. For
G D Em C Am F♯o B7
saw how e - vil and des - pair held them in a trance and
Christ the Lord Him-self hath said, those who will pre - pare may
I can see the gold-en streets in - side the east-ern gate my

GOT IT TOUGH, EH?

You have nothing to lose but your sleep.

21 JACOB'S LADDER

Traditional Negro Spiritual

2. EV'RY ROUND GOES HIGHER, HIGHER,
EV'RY ROUND GOES HIGHER, HIGHER,
EV'RY ROUND GOES HIGHER, HIGHER,
SOLDIER OF THE CROSS.

3. SINNER DO YOU LOVE YOUR JESUS,
SINNER DO YOU LOVE YOUR JESUS,
SINNER DO YOU LOVE YOUR JESUS,
SOLDIER OF THE CROSS.

22 ALL HAIL THE POWER OF JESUS' NAME

Edward Perronet

Oliver Holden

1. All hail the power of Je-sus' name! Let an-gels pros-trate fall;
2. Ye cho-sen seed of Is-rael's race, Ye ran-somed from the fall,
3. Let ev-ery kin-dred, ev-ery tribe, On this ter-res-trial ball,
4. O that with yon-der sa-cred throng We at His feet may fall!
Bring forth the roy-al di-a-dem, And crown Him Lord of all;
Hail Him who saves you by His grace, And crown Him Lord of all;
To Him all maj-es-ty as-cribe, And crown Him Lord of all;
We'll join the ev-er-last-ing song, And crown Him Lord of all;
Bring forth the roy-al di-a-dem, And crown Him Lord of all!
Hail Him who saves you by His grace, And crown Him Lord of all!
To Him all maj-es-ty as-cribe, And crown Him Lord of all!
We'll join the ev-er-last-ing song, And crown Him Lord of all!

we just couldn't keep it quiet.

23 GOD IS SO WONDERFUL

V. M. Virginia Marshall

Gently
*)
God is so Won-der-ful, __ I ___ can't ex-plain, But
I can say, "Glo-ry Hal-le-lu-jah! Praise His Ho-ly Name." Oh __
God is so Won-der-ful, __ I __ can't ex-plain, But I can say,
Alto Mel.
Ooo
rit. 2nd time
Fine
Melody
"Glo-ry Hal-le-lu-jah! Praise His Ho-ly Name."
It's won-der-ful _ be-cause He
(I) cast on Him _ my ev-'ry
Ooo

saved me, It's won-der-ful _ that He for-gave me _
bur - den, Lay at His feet _ my ev-'ry care ___ It's won-der-ful, won-der-ful,
1
2 D.C. al Fine
So ve - ry won-der-ful, won-der - ful that He is mine. I mine. Oh _
*) Cue notes optional on last time.

all your own,

very

You should know

24 HIS SHEEP AM I

O. J. Orien Johnson

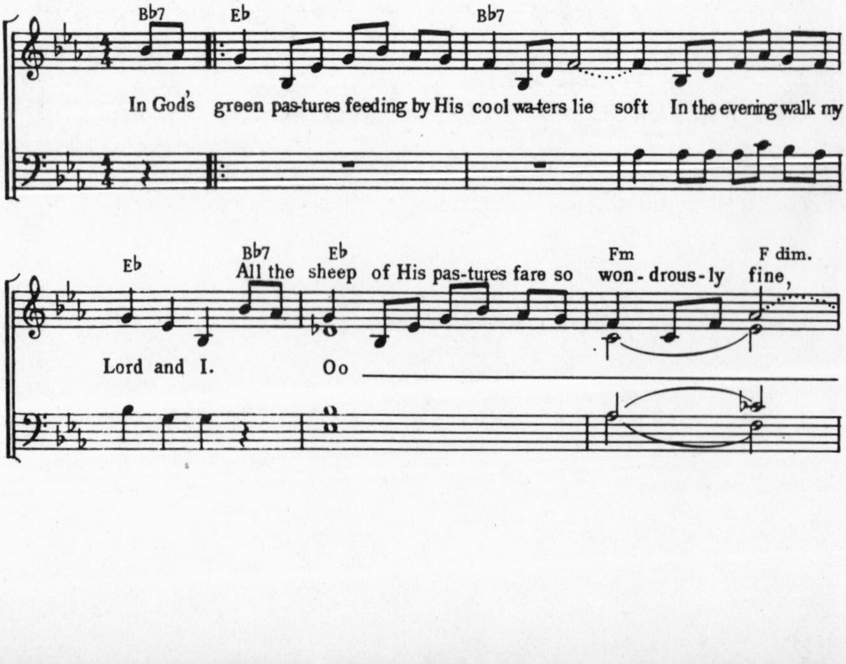
Bb7
Eb
Bb7
In God's green pas-tures feeding by His cool wa-ters lie soft In the evening walk my
Eb
Bb7
Eb
All the sheep of His pas-tures fare so
Fm
won - drous - ly
F dim.
fine,
Lord and I.
Oo

special

Eb Gm Bb7 Eb
His sheep am I.
Fine
Ab
His sheep am I. Wa-ters cool pas-tures
in the val-ley
Gm Fm Bb7 Eb
green In the eve - ning walk my Lord and I dark the
on the mountain in the eve-ning walk my Lord and I
Ab Gm C7 Fm Bb7 Eb
night rough the way step by step my Lord and I. In God's
in the val-ley on the mountain step by step, step by step my Lord and I.

the inside story

25 THE NUMBERS SONG

R. C.

Ralph Carmichael

Brightly
F Bb C7 F Gm C7
1. One is for the won - d'rous land in which we live,
F F7 Bb Bbm F C7 F
To the old Red White and Blue loy - al - ty we give.
Chorus
F A7 Dm Bb
Songs may come, songs may go, hap - pi - ness they bring;

Look at this.

2. TWO is for the tumult
sounding far and near,
But with freedom ringing
now we need never fear!
(to Chorus)

3. THREE is for the Wise Men
following the Star,
And today their wisdom
can guide us from afar!
(to Chorus)

4. FOUR is for the Blessed
City built Four Square,
What rejoicing there will be
when we get up there!

5. FIVE is for the little boy
with his loaves of bread,
When we all give thanks to Him
multitudes are fed!
(to Chorus)

6. SIX is for the long days
that we work and play,
But the next we set aside
to worship Him and pray!
(to Chorus)

7. SEVEN is the perfect
number, we are told.
Let's be more like seven
before we get too old!
(to Chorus)

Free!

26 PSALM 19

S. S.

Sonny Salsbury

learn the

facts of life

27 SONG OF THE SOUL SET FREE

Oswald J. Smith — A. H. Ackley

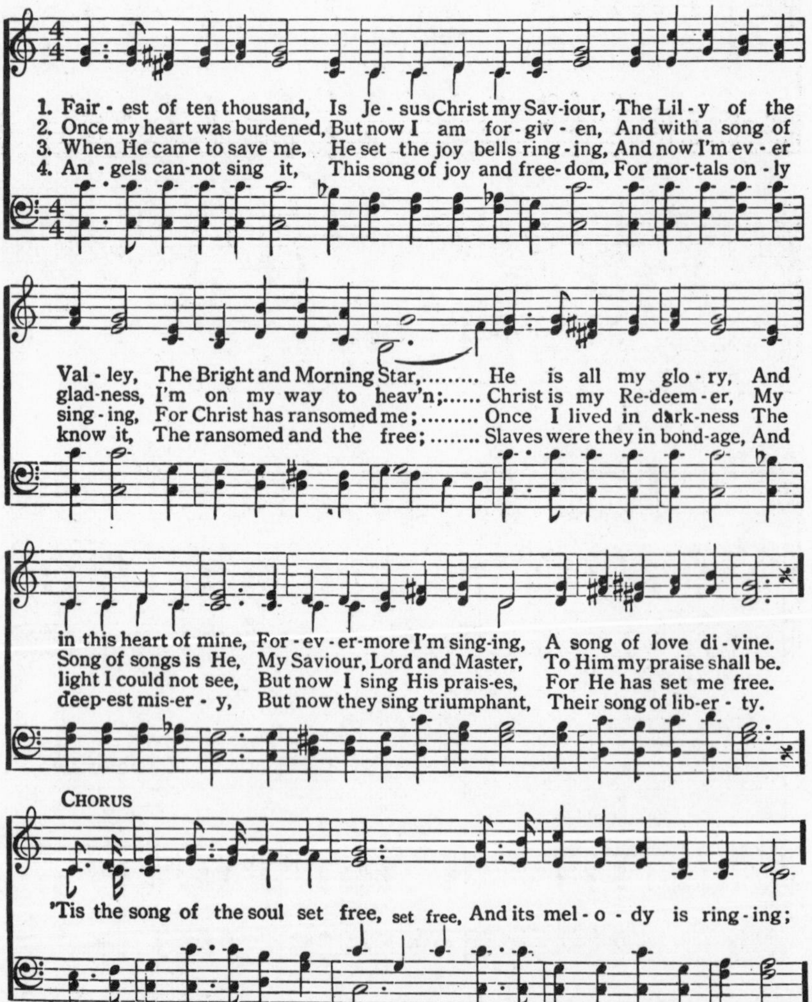
1. Fair - est of ten thousand, Is Je - sus Christ my Sav-iour, The Lil - y of the Val - ley, The Bright and Morning Star,......... He is all my glo - ry, And in this heart of mine, For - ev - er-more I'm sing-ing, A song of love di - vine.
2. Once my heart was burdened, But now I am for - giv - en, And with a song of glad-ness, I'm on my way to heav'n;...... Christ is my Re-deem - er, My Song of songs is He, My Saviour, Lord and Master, To Him my praise shall be.
3. When He came to save me, He set the joy bells ring - ing, And now I'm ev - er sing - ing, For Christ has ransomed me;......... Once I lived in dark-ness The light I could not see, But now I sing His prais-es, For He has set me free.
4. An - gels can-not sing it, This song of joy and free - dom, For mor-tals on - ly know it, The ransomed and the free;........ Slaves were they in bond-age, And deep-est mis-er - y, But now they sing triumphant, Their song of lib-er - ty.
CHORUS
'Tis the song of the soul set free, set free, And its mel - o - dy is ring - ing;

'Tis the song of the soul set free, set free, Joy and peace to me it's bring-ing,
'Tis the song of the soul set free, set free, And my heart is ev-er sing-ing Hal-le -
rit.
lu - - jah! Hal-le - lu - - jah! The song of the soul set free.
Hal - le - lu - jah! Hal - le - lu - jah!

hear what all the raves are about:

It happens every generation.

28 TO GOD BE THE GLORY

Fanny J. Crosby — W. H. Doane

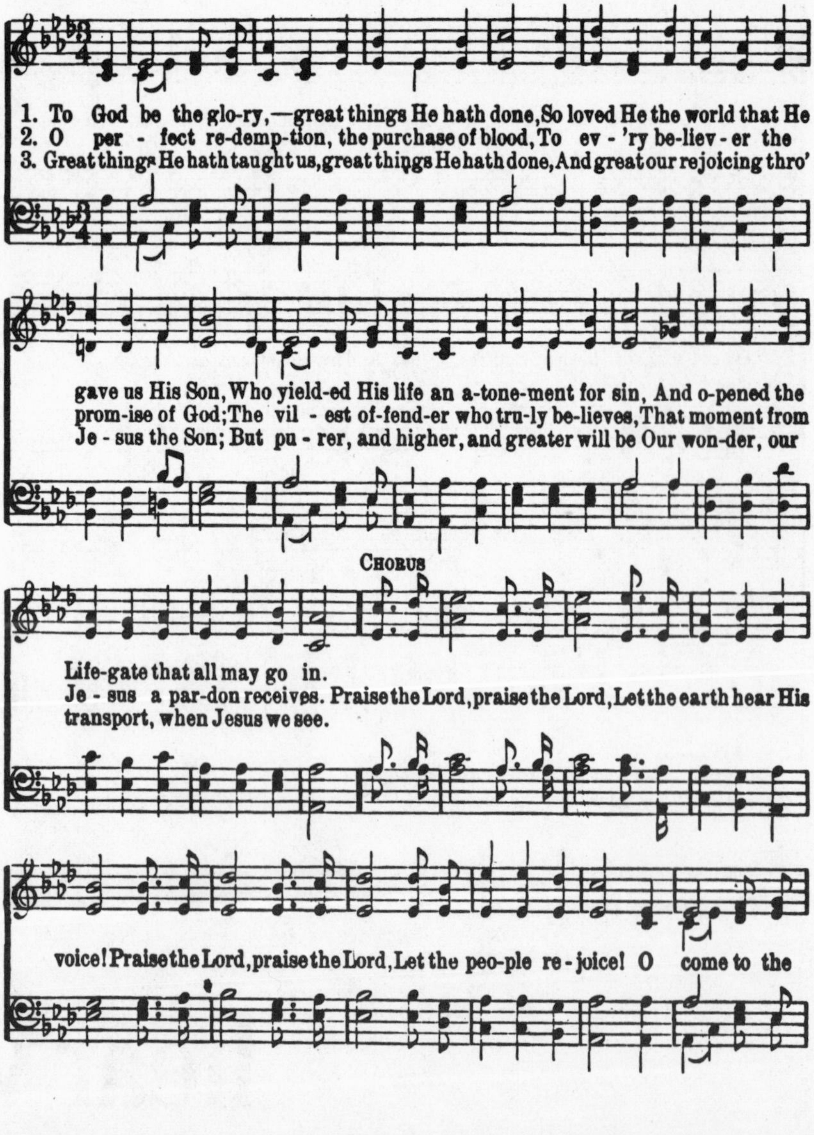
1. To God be the glo-ry,—great things He hath done, So loved He the world that He
2. O per - fect re-demp-tion, the purchase of blood, To ev - 'ry be-liev - er the
3. Great things He hath taught us, great things He hath done, And great our rejoicing thro'
gave us His Son, Who yield-ed His life an a-tone-ment for sin, And o-pened the
prom-ise of God; The vil - est of-fend-er who tru-ly be-lieves, That moment from
Je - sus the Son; But pu - rer, and higher, and greater will be Our won-der, our
CHORUS
Life-gate that all may go in.
Je - sus a par-don receives. Praise the Lord, praise the Lord, Let the earth hear His
transport, when Jesus we see.
voice! Praise the Lord, praise the Lord, Let the peo-ple re - joice! O come to the

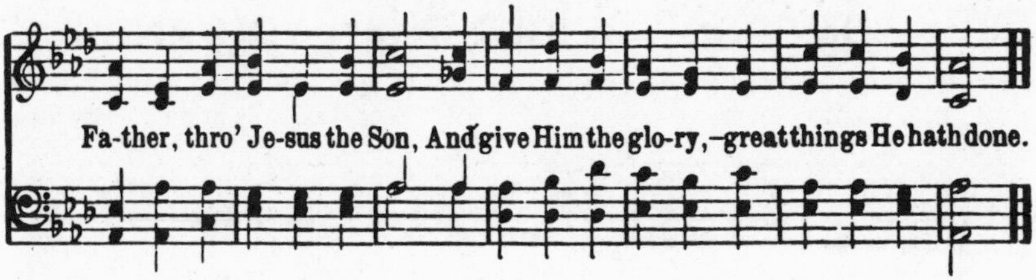
Fa-ther, thro' Je-sus the Son, And give Him the glo-ry,—great things He hath done.

29 FOR GOD SO LOVED THE WORLD

Frances Townsend

Alfred B. Smith

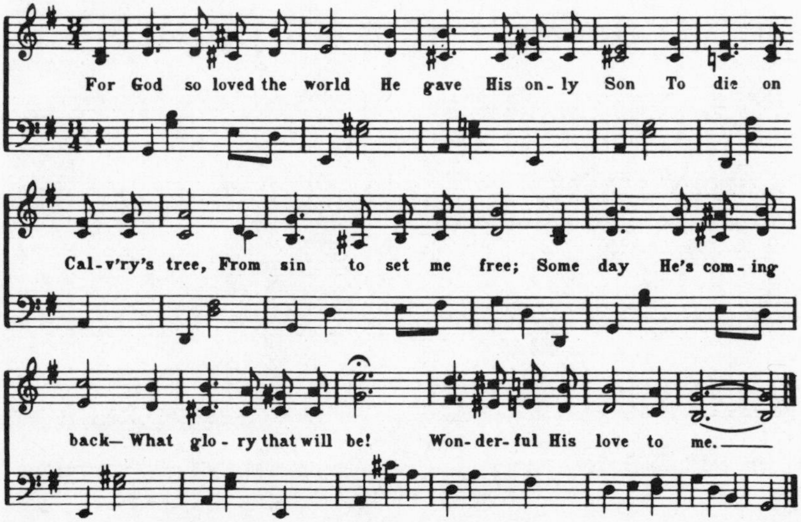
For God so loved the world He gave His on-ly Son To die on
Cal-v'ry's tree, From sin to set me free; Some day He's com-ing
back— What glo-ry that will be! Won-der-ful His love to me.

Elementary, my dear Watson.

30 SOMEBODY BIGGER THAN YOU AND I

J. L., H. H. & S. B. — Johnny Lange, Hy Heath & Sonny Burke

Moderato (with much feeling)
mf
CHORUS
Eb Ebmaj7 Cm Gm A7 Ab9 Eb Fm7 Bb7
Who made the moun-tain, who made the tree, Who made the riv-er flow to the sea, And
Cm Gm Abmaj7 Eb Cm Cm7 F7 Bb7
who hung the moon in the star-ry sky? SOME-BOD-Y BIG-GER THAN YOU AND I.
Eb Ebmaj7 Cm Gm A7 Ab9 Eb Cb7 Fm7 Bb7
Who makes the flow-ers bloom in the spring, Who writes the song for the rob-in to sing, And
Cm Gm Abmaj7 Cb7 Eb Cm
who sends the rain when the earth is dry? SOME-BOD-Y BIG-GER THAN

A MAN FOR ALL SEASONS

F7 Bb7 Eb Fm7 Bb7-9 Eb Fm7 Gm Cm7 Fm7 Bb7-9 Eb Ebm
YOU AND I— He lights the way when the road is long. Keeps you com-pan - y. With
Bb Gm7 Bbmaj7 Bb6 Cm Cm7 F7 Fm7 Bb7
love to guide you He walks be-side you. Just like he walks with me.
Eb Ebmaj7 Cm Gm A7 Ab9 Eb Cb7 Fm7 Bb7
When I am wear-y, Filled with des-pair, Who gives me cour-age to go on from there. And
Cm Gm Ab Cb7 Eb Cm
who gives me faith that will nev-er die? SOME-BOD-Y BIG-GER THAN
Fm Fm7 Eb Fm7 Bb7-9 Eb Cb Eb
YOU AND I— I—
rit.

31 IT'S A WONDERFUL DAY

J. O.

Jim Owens

CUSTOMERS
WANTED

can't help sing-in' what a won-der-ful day! Since I found the Lord!

32 EVERY DAY WITH JESUS

Robert C. Loveless

Wendell P. Loveless

Ev-'ry day with Je-sus Is sweet-er than the day be-fore,
Ev-'ry day with Je - sus, Sweet-er than be-
Ev-'ry day with Je-sus, I love Him more and more;
fore, Ev - 'ry day with Je-sus, love Him more and
Je-sus saves and keeps me, And He's the One I'm wait-ing for;
more; Je - sus saves and keeps me, I am wait-ing;
Ev-'ry day with Je-sus Is sweet-er than the day be - fore.

made for each other

There's one in every crowd!

33 I MAY NEVER PASS THIS WAY AGAIN

M. W. & I. M. — Murray Wizell & Irving Melsher

Moderately, with warm expression
Piano
mf
Refrain
C Em7 E♭dim Dm7 G7 C
I'll give my hand to those who can-not see The sun-rise or the
mp-mf
Gm Gm7 A7 Gm6 A7 Dm Dm7 G7 C G♯dim
fall - ing rain. I'll sing my song, to cheer the wea - ry a -
Am Am7 D7 Am7 D7 Dm7 G7
long, For I MAY NEV - ER PASS THIS WAY A - GAIN.

C Em7 E♭dim Dm7 G7 C
I'll share my faith with ev-'ry trou-bled heart, So I shall not have
C7 F A7 Dm A F6
lived in vain. I'll give my hand,
Cmaj7 G♯dim Am Am7 F6 C♯dim Dm G7 Am Fm6
I'll sing my song, I'll share my faith be-cause I know
cresc.
G7 Dm7 G7 C C+ C6 C+
That the time is now, To ful-fill each vow, For I
C D7 G7 1.C6 Dm7 G7(-9 +5) 2.C Fmaj7 F6 C6
MAY NEV-ER PASS THIS WAY A-GAIN. GAIN.
rall.

not far from where
you are, right now.

34 PEACE IN THE VALLEY

T. A. D. Thomas A. Dorsey

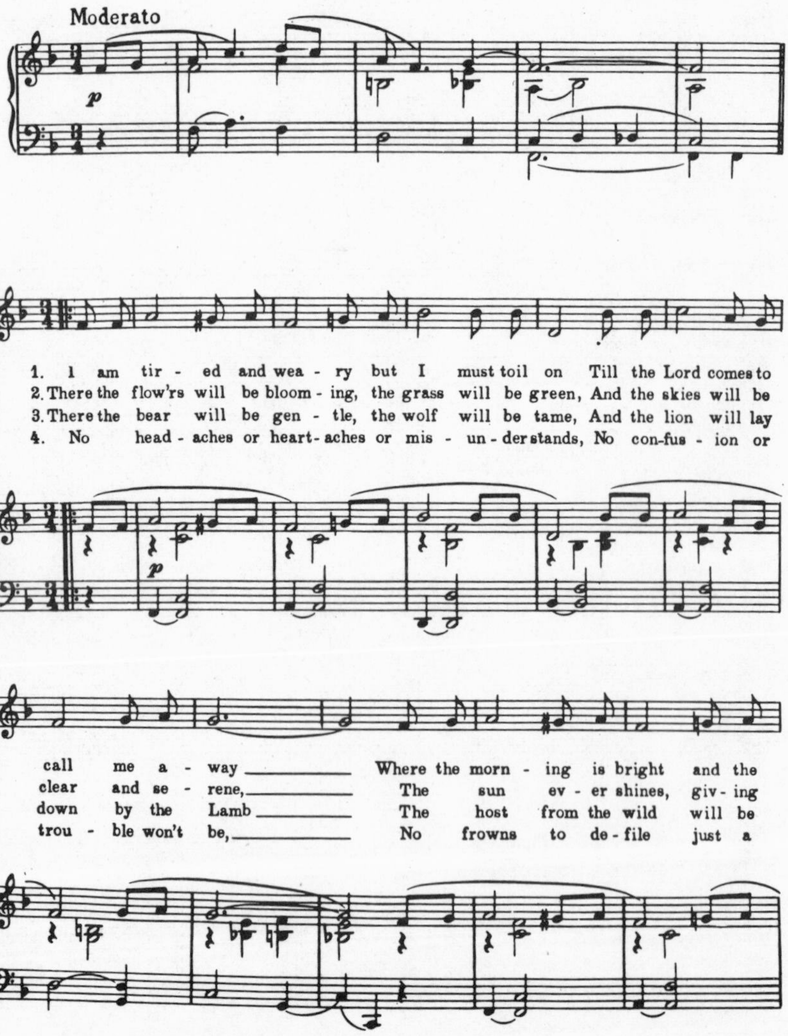
Moderato
p
1. I am tir - ed and wea - ry but I must toil on Till the Lord comes to
2. There the flow'rs will be bloom - ing, the grass will be green, And the skies will be
3. There the bear will be gen - tle, the wolf will be tame, And the lion will lay
4. No head - aches or heart - aches or mis - un - der stands, No con - fus - ion or
p
call me a - way Where the morn - ing is bright and the
clear and se - rene, The sun ev - er shines, giv - ing
down by the Lamb The host from the wild will be
trou - ble won't be, No frowns to de - file just a

Lamb is the light And the night is as fair as the day.
one end-less beam And no clouds there will ev-er be seen.
led by a Child, I'll be changed from the crea-ture I am.
big end-less smile, There'll be peace and con-tent-ment for me.
CHORUS
There'll be peace in the val-ley for me some-day, There'll be peace in the val-ley for
me. I pray no more sor-row and sad-ness or trou-ble will be, There'll be
peace in the val-ley for me.
1-2-3
4
me.

Help yourself!

It's about time you woke up

35 NEW LIFE IN CHRIST

J. W. P. John W. Peterson

Intro.
1. Gone is the guilt of my sin, (my sin,) Peace is now reign-ing with - in; (with-in;) Since I be- lieved- par - don re-ceived- Hap-py, so hap- py I've been. (I've been.)
2. Bright-er the jour-ney each day, (each day,) Tho there is much to dis - may; (dis-may;) Heav- en a - waits- bright pearl-y gates- There at the end of the way. (the way.)
3. Come with your sin-bur-dened heart, (sad heart,) Christ will His cleans-ing im - part; (im-part;) He will for- give- in Him you'll live- O how the joy-bells will start. (will start.)

EYE-OPENER

Did you take a good look in a mirror today?

Chorus

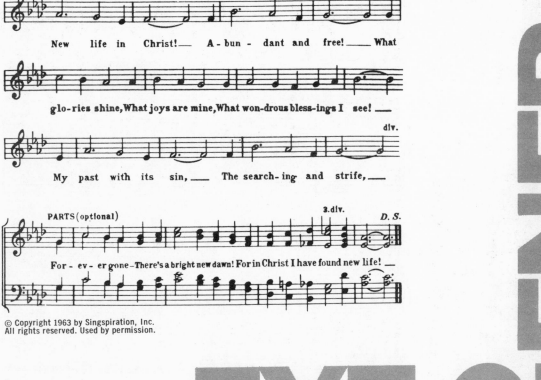

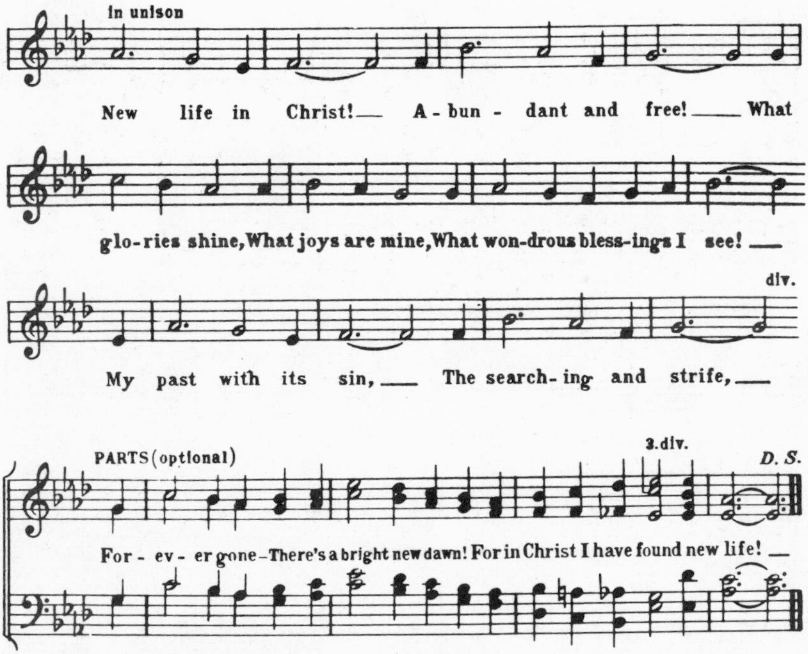
in unison
New life in Christ! — A-bun-dant and free! — What
glo-ries shine, What joys are mine, What won-drous bless-ings I see! —
div.
My past with its sin, — The search-ing and strife, —
PARTS (optional)
3.div.
D. S.
For-ev-er gone - There's a bright new dawn! For in Christ I have found new life! —

Unusual

36 GOOD NEWS, CHARIOT'S COMIN'

Traditional Negro Spiritual

Bb Eb Bb Eb Bb
GET UP IN THE CHAR - I - OT. CAR - RY ME HOME.
p
Eb Bb Eb Bb Eb
GET UP IN THE CHAR - I - OT. CHAR - RY ME HOME AN' I
mf
f
Bb Bb+ Eb F7 Bb D. C.
DON'T WANT HER LEAVE - A ME BE - - HIND.

2. THERE'S A LONG WHITE ROBE IN THE HEAVEN I KNOW
LONG WHITE ROBE IN THE HEAVEN KNOW
LONG WHITE ROBE IN THE HEAVEN KNOW
AN'I DON'T WANT HER LEAVE-A ME BEHIND

3. THERE'S A GOLDEN HARP IN THE HEAVEN I KNOW.
GOLDEN HARP IN THE HEAVEN I KNOW
GOLDEN HARP IN THE HEAVEN I KNOW
AN'I WANT HER LEAVE-A ME BEHIND.

offer.

enjoy all the advantages

37 POOR WAYFARIN' STRANGER

Traditional

Slowly
G6
D7
1. Solo I am a poor way-far-in' strang-er, A trav'lin' through this world of
p
pp
(Humming)
pp
G6
woe. But there's no sick - ness, toil, nor dan-ger in that bright
D7
G6
land to — which I go, I'm go-ing there — to see my
Em
Am
B +
B
C
fa-ther; I'm go-ing there no more to roam, I'm just a -

G6 D7 Em
going over Jor- dan, I'm just a - go - ing over home.

2. I know dark clouds will gather 'round me,
I know my way is rough and steep,
But golden fields lie out before me
Where God's redeemed no more shall weep.
I'm going there to see my mother,
She said she'd meet me when I come;
I'm just a-going over Jordan,
I'm just a-going over home.

3. I'll soon be free from ev'ry trial,
My body sleep in the old churchyard.
I'll drop the cross of self-denial
And enter on my great reward.
I'm going there to see my Saviour,
To sing His praise for evermore;
I'm just a-going over Jordan,
I'm just a-going over home.

38 MICHAEL, ROW THE BOAT ASHORE

Traditional Negro Spiritual

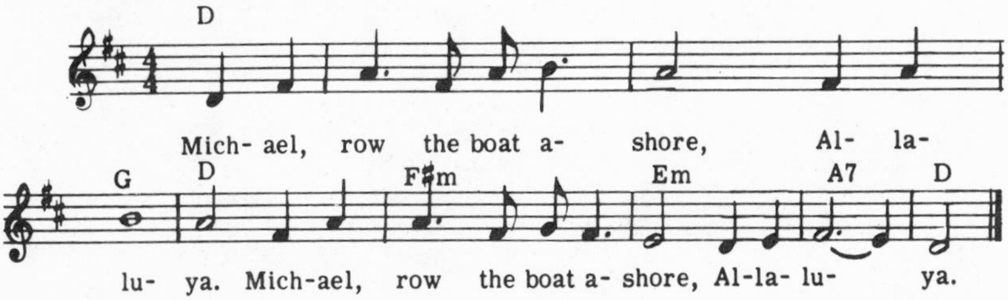
D
Mich- ael, row the boat a- shore, Al- la-
G D F♯m Em A7 D
lu- ya. Mich-ael, row the boat a- shore, Al-la- lu- ya.

Michael's boat is a music boat,
Allaluya,
Michael's boat is a music boat,
Allaluya.

Michael, row the boat ashore, etc.

Sister help to trim the sail,
Allaluya,
Sister help to trim the sail,
Allaluya.

Michael, row the boat ashore, etc.

Jordan's River is deep and wide,
Allaluya,
Meet my mother on the other side,
Allaluya.

Michael, row the boat ashore, etc.

Jordan's River is chilly and cold,
Allaluya,
Kills the body but not the soul,
Allaluya.

Michael, row the boat ashore, etc.

Come

39 WHAT THIS WORLD NEEDS

K. K. Kurt Kaiser

G Em Am D7
1. What This World Needs is love shown toward my
2. Why must there al - ways be this ra - cial
3. I know the One who'll solve this old world's
G Am7 D7 G
broth - er. 'Swhat it needs, What This World
trou - ble? Tell me why. When will we
prob - lems. Yes I do. But we must
Em Am D7 G C
Needs is love to stop this hate. 'Swhat it
learn, a - lone we can't sur - vive, Stay a -
give him half a chance to try. Just a
F7 B♭ Gm Cm7 F7 Dm7
needs, Ev - 'ry - where all a - round us there is fight - ing,
live, While our own boys are giv - ing all they have to
try, No oth - er one can bring us peace and give re -
G7 Am7 D7 G Em
curs - ing, hat - ing, ly - ing; What This World Needs is
save the free - dom we hold dear, let us not be
lief from all these ten - sions, oh that you knew Him,
Am7 D7 Bm B♭ Am7
love, more love for all, for all.
fight - ing an - y - more, no more.
loved Him, served Him too, please do.
D7 1-2 G Am7 D7
3 G F
Love, more love.

Will it ever catch on?

40 LIKE A RIVER GLORIOUS

Frances R. Havergal — J. Mountain

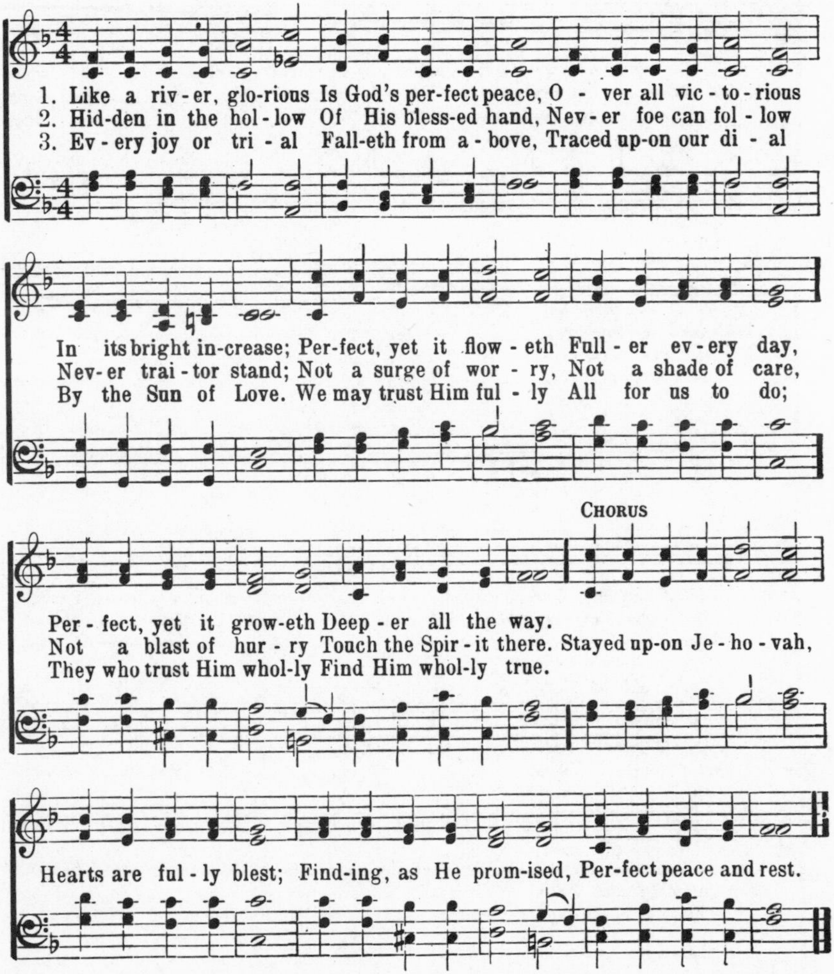
1. Like a riv-er, glo-rious Is God's per-fect peace, O - ver all vic-to-rious
2. Hid-den in the hol-low Of His bless-ed hand, Nev-er foe can fol-low
3. Ev-ery joy or tri-al Fall-eth from a-bove, Traced up-on our di-al
In its bright in-crease; Per-fect, yet it flow-eth Full-er ev-ery day,
Nev-er trai-tor stand; Not a surge of wor-ry, Not a shade of care,
By the Sun of Love. We may trust Him ful-ly All for us to do;
CHORUS
Per-fect, yet it grow-eth Deep-er all the way.
Not a blast of hur-ry Touch the Spir-it there. Stayed up-on Je-ho-vah,
They who trust Him whol-ly Find Him whol-ly true.
Hearts are ful-ly blest; Find-ing, as He prom-ised, Per-fect peace and rest.

yes

41 HEAVEN CAME DOWN, AND GLORY FILLED MY SOUL

J. P.

John Peterson

Brightly
1. O what a won-der-ful, won-der-ful day, Day I will
2. Born of the Spir-it with life from a-bove In-to God's
3. Now I've a hope that will sure-ly en-dure Af-ter the
nev-er for-get; After I'd wan-dered in dark-ness a-way,
fam-'ly di-vine, Jus-ti-fied ful-ly thro' Cal-va-ry's love,
pass-ing of time; I have a fu-ture in Heav-en for sure,
Je-sus my Sav-ior I met. O what a ten-der com-
O what a stand-ing is mine! And the tran-sac-tion so
There in those man-sions sub-lime. And it's be-cause of that
pas-sion-ate friend, He met the need of my heart; Shad-ows dis-
quick-ly was made When as a sin-ner I came, Took of the
won-der-ful day, When at the cross I be-lieved; Rich-es e-

pel - ling, With joy I am tell-ing, He made all the dark-ness de - part!
of - fer Of grace He did prof-fer — He saved me, O praise His dear name!
ter - nal And bless-ings su - per-nal From His pre-cious hand I re-ceived.
CHORUS
Heav - en came down and glo - ry filled my soul,
When at the cross the Sav - ior made me whole; My
sins were washed a - way, And my night was turned to
day — Heav - en came down and glo - ry filled my soul!

country?

making it beautiful

42 THIS IS MY COUNTRY

Don Raye

Al Jacobs

wasn't enough

Check it out.

43 THERE'S ROOM AT THE CROSS FOR YOU

I. S. Ira Stanphill

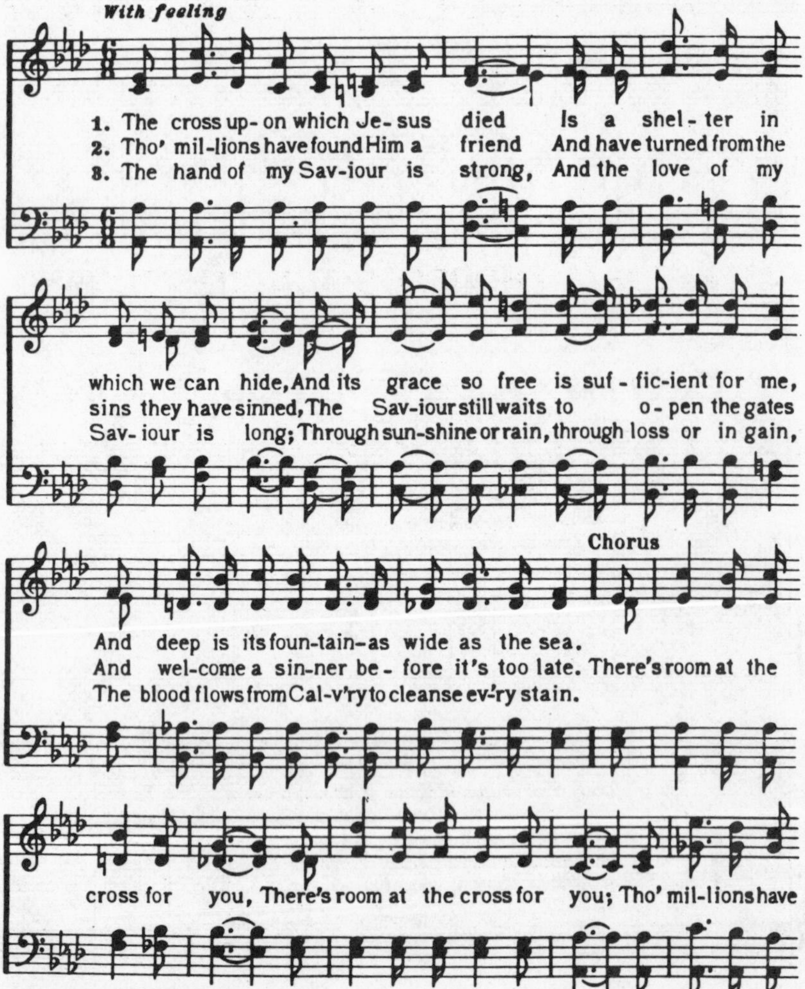
With feeling
1. The cross up-on which Je-sus died Is a shel-ter in which we can hide, And its grace so free is suf-fic-ient for me, And deep is its foun-tain-as wide as the sea.
2. Tho' mil-lions have found Him a friend And have turned from the sins they have sinned, The Sav-iour still waits to o-pen the gates And wel-come a sin-ner be-fore it's too late.
3. The hand of my Sav-iour is strong, And the love of my Sav-iour is long; Through sun-shine or rain, through loss or in gain, The blood flows from Cal-v'ry to cleanse ev'-ry stain.
Chorus
There's room at the cross for you, There's room at the cross for you; Tho' mil-lions have

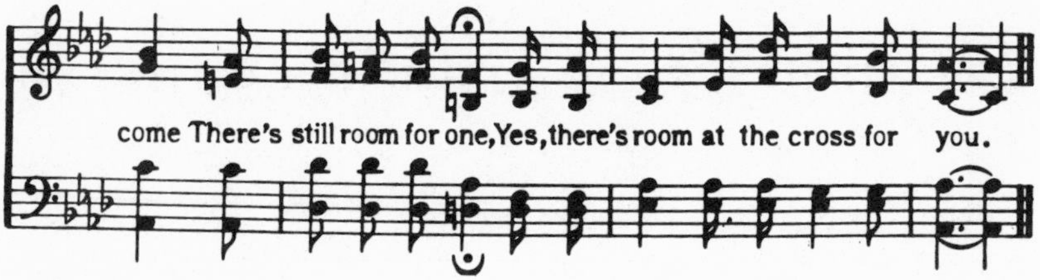
come There's still room for one, Yes, there's room at the cross for you.

44 O FOR A THOUSAND TONGUES TO SING

Charles Wesley — Carl G. Blaser

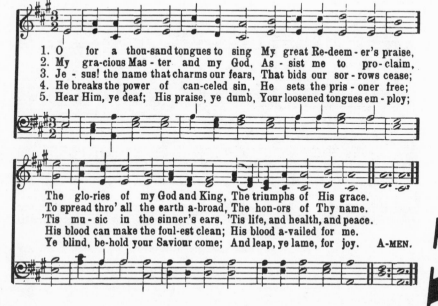

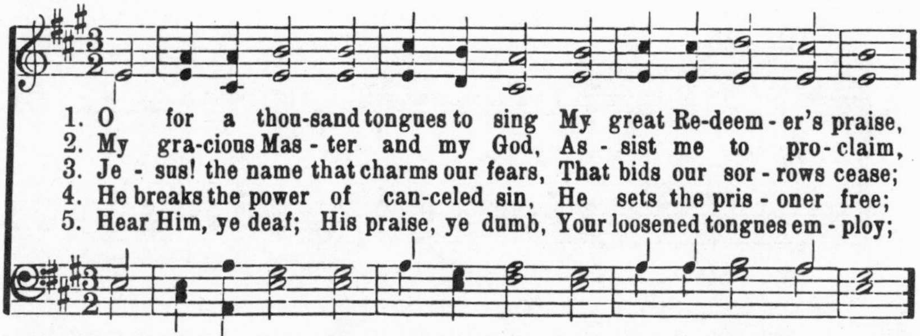
1. O for a thou-sand tongues to sing My great Re-deem - er's praise,
2. My gra-cious Mas - ter and my God, As - sist me to pro- claim,
3. Je - sus! the name that charms our fears, That bids our sor - rows cease;
4. He breaks the power of can-celed sin, He sets the pris - oner free;
5. Hear Him, ye deaf; His praise, ye dumb, Your loosened tongues em - ploy;
The glo-ries of my God and King, The triumphs of His grace.
To spread thro' all the earth a-broad, The hon-ors of Thy name.
'Tis mu - sic in the sinner's ears, 'Tis life, and health, and peace.
His blood can make the foul-est clean; His blood a-vailed for me.
Ye blind, be-hold your Saviour come; And leap, ye lame, for joy. A-MEN.

You can't lose

"This is your Captain"

45 HE'S A MIGHTY BIG GOD

O. S. | Otis Skillings

Maybe you should talk to him!

Won't rust, burn,

46 SWING LOW, SWEET CHARIOT

Traditional Negro Spiritual

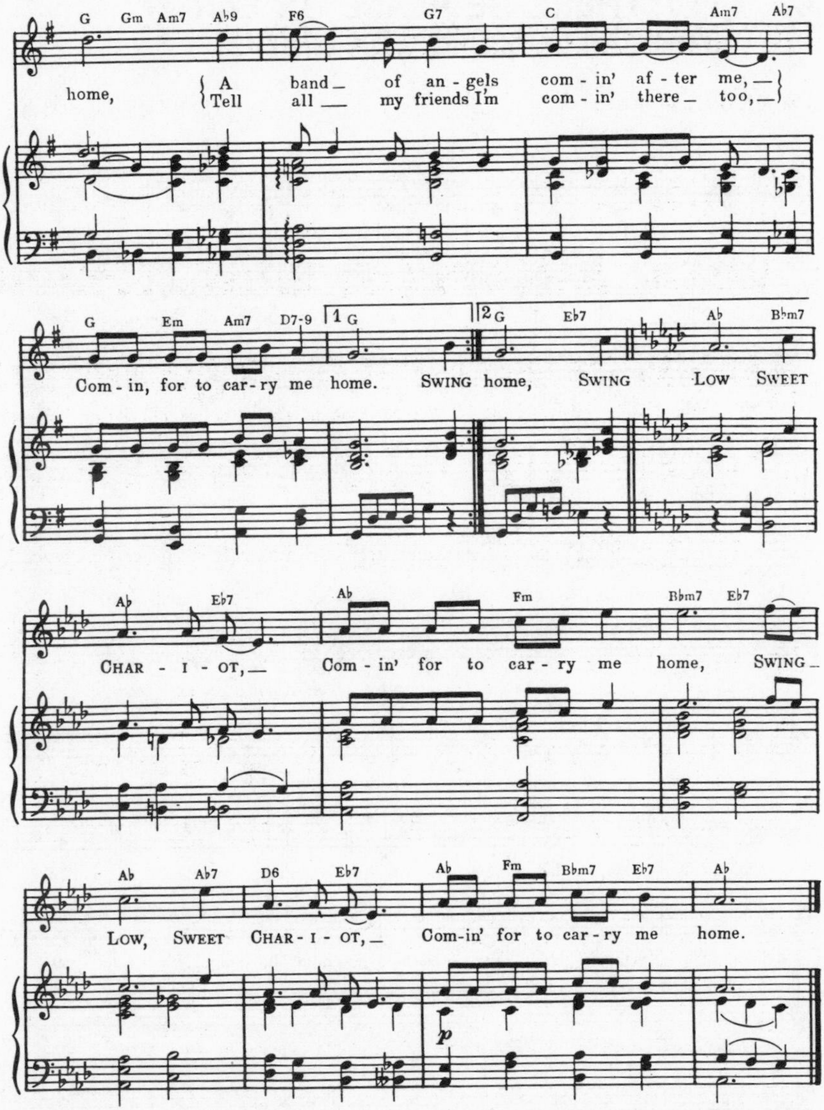
G Gm Am7 A♭9 F6 G7 C Am7 A♭7
home, { A band — of an - gels com - in' af - ter me, — }
{ Tell all — my friends I'm com - in' there — too, — }
G Em Am7 D7-9 1 G 2 G E♭7 A♭ B♭m7
Com - in, for to car - ry me home. SWING home, SWING LOW SWEET
A♭ E♭7 A♭ Fm B♭m7 E♭7
CHAR - I - OT, — Com - in' for to car - ry me home, SWING —
A♭ A♭7 D6 E♭7 A♭ Fm B♭m7 E♭7 A♭
LOW, SWEET CHAR - I - OT, — Com - in' for to car - ry me home.

rot, warp...

have what it takes
Do you

47 LET THERE BE PEACE ON EARTH
(And Let It Begin with Me)

S. M. & J. J.

Sy Miller & Jill Jackson

1.
2.
Let there be peace on earth And let it be - gin with
me; Let there be peace on earth, The
peace that was meant to be. With God as our
Fa - ther, Broth - ers all are we.
Let me walk with my broth - er In per - fect har - mo -
ny. Let peace be - gin with me, Let
this be the mo - ment now. With ev - 'ry
step I take, Let this be my sol - emn vow: To
take each mo - ment and live each mo - ment In peace e - ter - nal -
ly. Let there be peace on earth And
let it be - gin with me. Let it be - gin with me.

48 LET US BREAK BREAD TOGETHER

Traditional Negro Spiritual

Let us break bread to - geth - er on our knees, Let us
break bread to - geth - er on our knees; When I fall on my
knees with my face to the ris - ing sun, O Lord, have mer - cy on
Fine
me. Let us take the cup to - geth - er on our knees,
Let us take the cup to - geth - er on our knees; When I
fall on my knees with my face to the ris - ing sun, O Lord, have
mer - cy on me. Let us praise God to - geth - er on our
D.S. al Fine
knees, Let us praise God to - geth - er on our knees;

why not get the best

We wouldn't put our name on it

49 AMEN

Traditional

D
A - - MEN! A - - MEN
D G D G D A7
1. See the lit - tle ba - by
A - MEN, A - MEN, A - MEN! (Continue reading notes stem down.)
1. Wrapped in a man-ger
2. Talk-in' with the eld-ers
On Sun - day morn - in'
To-mor-row there is wis - dom
D
A MEN A - MEN.
D G D G D A7
1. See Him in the tem-ple
D. S.
A - MEN, A - MEN, A - MEN.
D Bb7 Eb
1. John bap - tiz - in'
2. Talk - in' with the fish-er-men
MEN. A - MEN.
And sav - in' all the sin - ners
And mak - in' dis-cip - les
Eb Ab
A - - MEN. A -

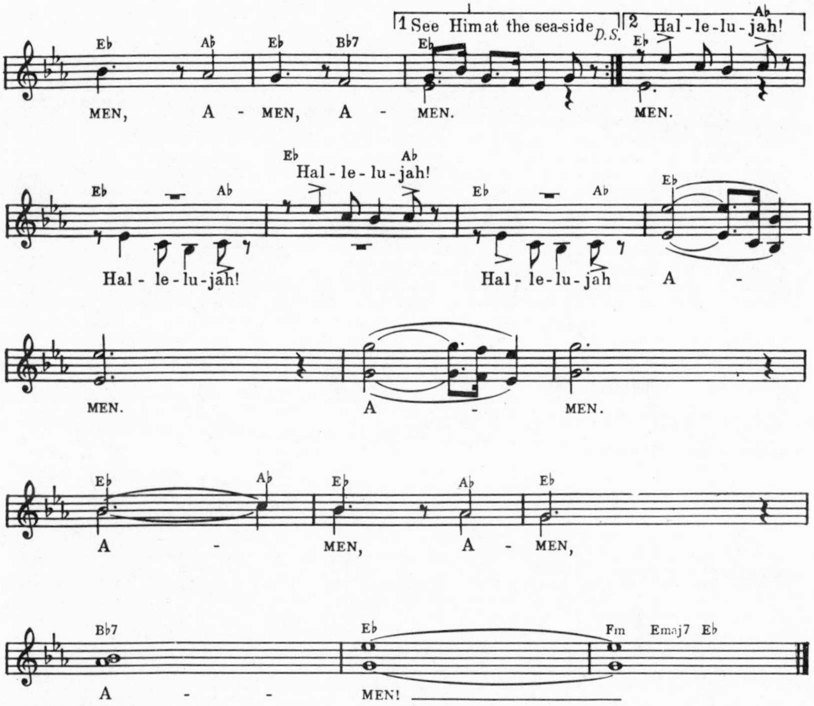
1 See Him at the sea-side D.S.
2 Hal-le-lu-jah!
Eb Ab Eb Bb7 Eb Eb Ab
MEN, A - MEN, A - MEN. MEN.
Eb Ab
Hal-le-lu-jah!
Eb Ab Eb Ab Eb
Hal-le-lu-jah! Hal-le-lu-jah A -
MEN. A - MEN.
Eb Ab Eb Ab Eb
A - MEN, A - MEN,
Bb7 Eb Fm Emaj7 Eb
A - - MEN!

if we didn't mean it.

50 THE SAVIOR IS WAITING

R. C. — Ralph Carmichael

The Savior is waiting to enter your heart.
(If) you'll take one step t'ward the Savior my friend,
Why don't you let Him come in. There's nothing in
You'll find His arms open wide. Recieve Him and
this world to keep you apart. What is your
all of your darkness will end. Within your

an - swer to Him.
heart He'll a - bide.
Time af - ter time He has
wait - ed be - fore And now He is wait - ing a - gain.
To see if you're will - ing to o - pen the door.
1
2
Oh how He wants to come in.
If in

Go ahead.

a good deal.
than just

51 JESUS IS COMING AGAIN

J. W. P. John W. Peterson

1. Mar-vel-ous mes-sage we bring, Glo-ri-ous car-ol we sing,
2. For-est and flow-er ex-claim, Moun-tain and mead-ow the same,
3. Stand-ing be-fore Him at last, Tri-al and trou-ble all past,
Won-der-ful word of the King, Je-sus is com-ing a-gain! (a-gain!)
All earth and heav-en pro-claim, Je-sus is com-ing a-gain! (a-gain!)
Crowns at His feet we will cast, Je-sus is com-ing a-gain! (a-gain!)
CHORUS
Com-ing a-gain, Com-ing a-gain;
May-be morn-ing, may-be noon, May-be eve-ning and may-be soon!

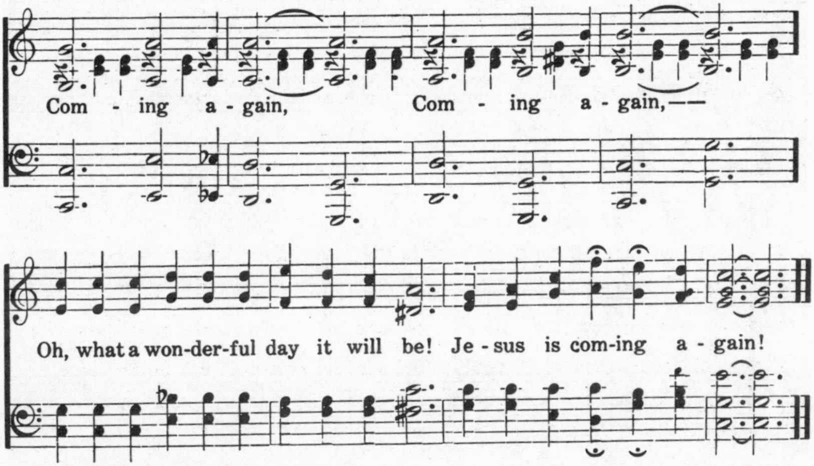
Com - ing a - gain, Com - ing a - gain,—
Oh, what a won-der-ful day it will be! Je - sus is com-ing a - gain!

It means a good deal more

52 HE'S GOT THE WHOLE WORLD IN HIS HANDS

Traditional Negro Spiritual

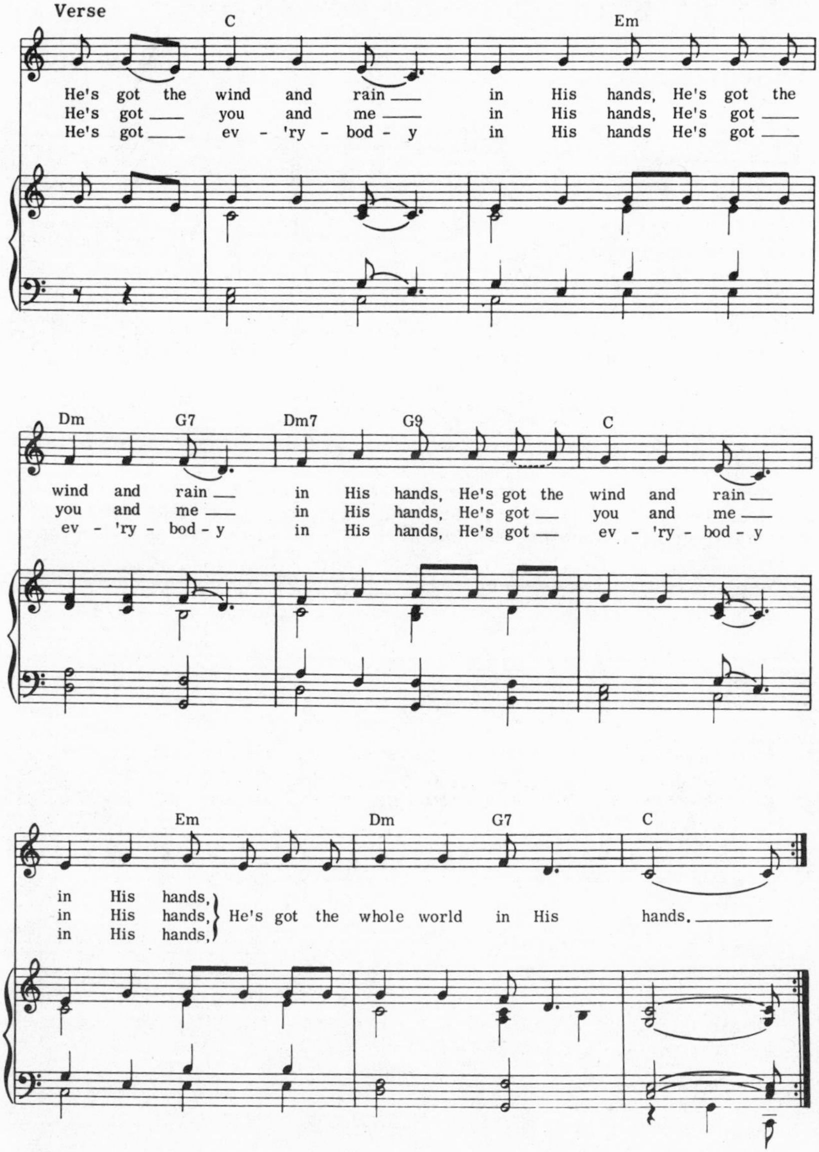
Verse
C
Em
He's got the wind and rain in His hands, He's got the
He's got you and me in His hands, He's got
He's got ev - 'ry - bod - y in His hands He's got
Dm
G7
Dm7
G9
C
wind and rain in His hands, He's got the wind and rain
you and me in His hands, He's got you and me
ev - 'ry - bod - y in His hands, He's got ev - 'ry - bod - y
Em
Dm
G7
C
in His hands,
in His hands,
in His hands,
He's got the whole world in His hands.

Get into this world.

53 SPRINGS OF LIVING WATER

J. W. P. John W. Peterson

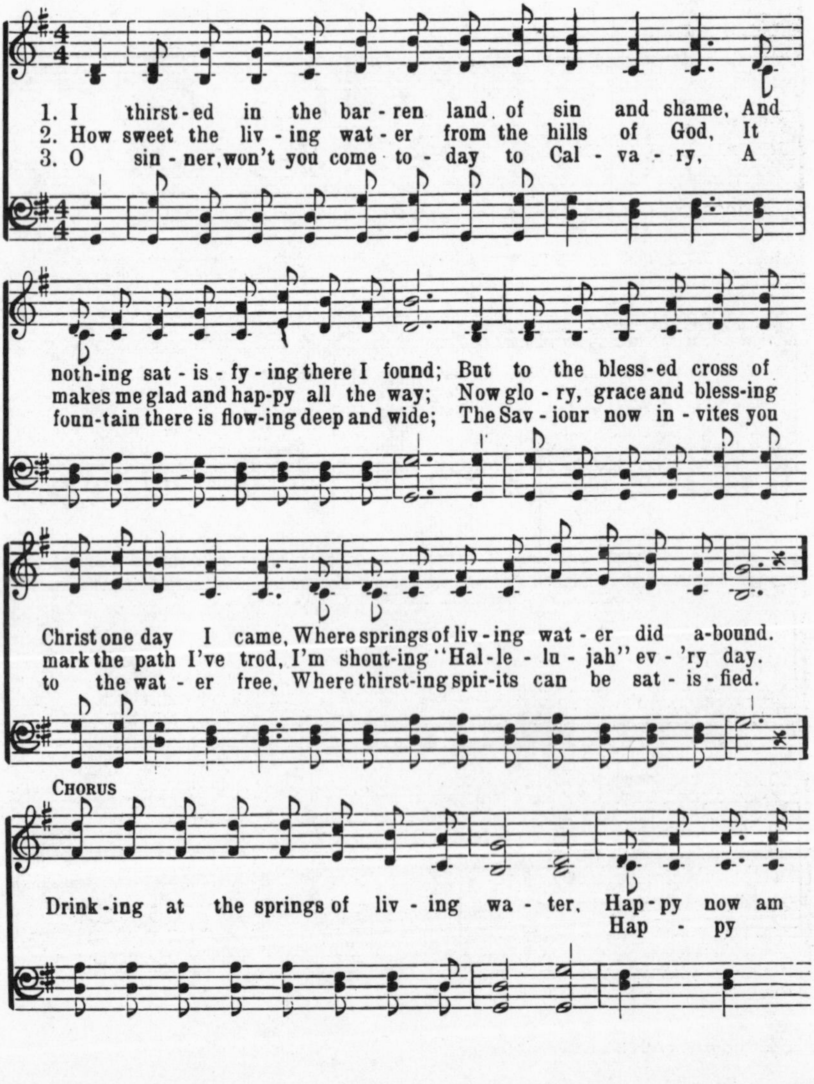
1. I thirst-ed in the bar-ren land of sin and shame, And
2. How sweet the liv-ing wat-er from the hills of God, It
3. O sin-ner, won't you come to-day to Cal-va-ry, A
noth-ing sat-is-fy-ing there I found; But to the bless-ed cross of
makes me glad and hap-py all the way; Now glo-ry, grace and bless-ing
foun-tain there is flow-ing deep and wide; The Sav-iour now in-vites you
Christ one day I came, Where springs of liv-ing wat-er did a-bound.
mark the path I've trod, I'm shout-ing "Hal-le-lu-jah" ev-'ry day.
to the wat-er free, Where thirst-ing spir-its can be sat-is-fied.
CHORUS
Drink-ing at the springs of liv-ing wa-ter, Hap-py now am
Hap - py

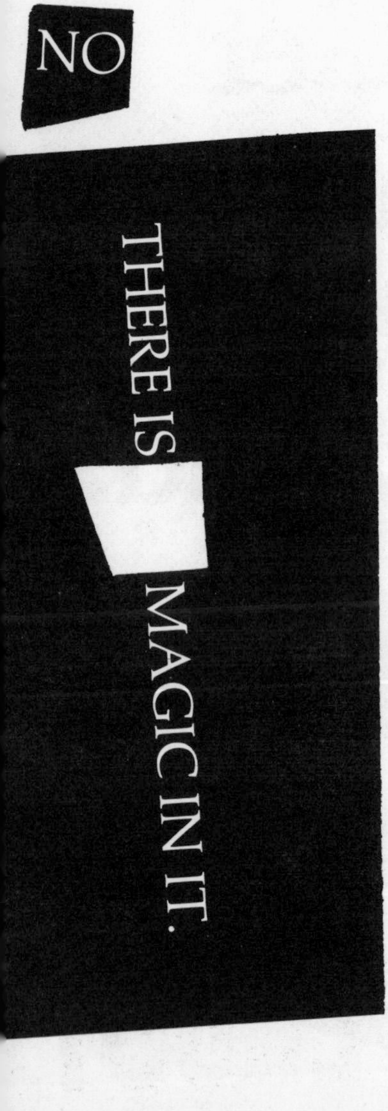
NO
THERE IS
MAGIC IN IT.

I, My soul they sat - is - fy; Drink-ing at the
now am I, My soul they sat - is - fy; I'm
springs of liv-ing wa - ter, O won-der-ful and boun-ti - ful sup - ply.

54 HAPPY AM I

C. E. Clayton Erb

mf
Hap-py am I; Je-sus loves me, He took my sins and He made me free.
Now I'm sing-ing a joy-ful song, so hap-py am I.

ENJOY

They helped start a revolution

55 LITTLE DAVID, PLAY ON YOUR HARP

Traditional Negro Spiritual

Lively
mf
Lit-tle Dav-id play on your harp, Hal-le - lu, Hal-le - lu; Lit-tle Dav-id
play on your harp, Hal - le - lu. ___ Lit-tle Dav-id play on your
harp, Hal-le - lu, Hal-le - lu; Lit-tle Dav-id play on your harp, Hal - le -
1.
2. Fine
lu. ___ Lit-tle —
Dav - id was a shep-herd boy, He
Josh - ua was the son of Nun, He

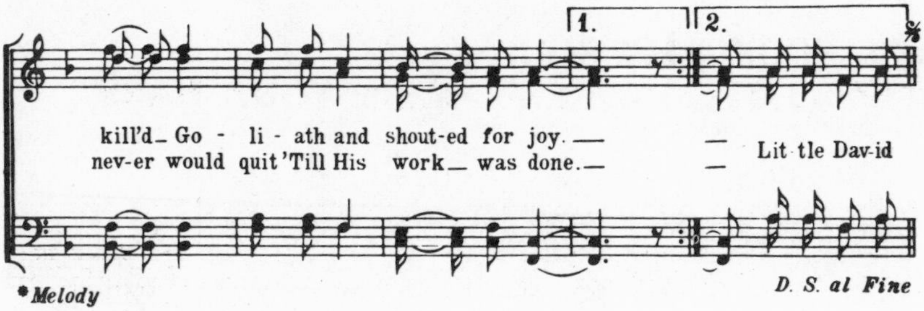
1.
2.
kill'd_ Go - li - ath and shout-ed for joy. —
nev-er would quit 'Till His work_ was done. —
Lit tle Dav-id
*Melody
D. S. al Fine

56 ON TOP OF OLD SMOKEY

Traditional

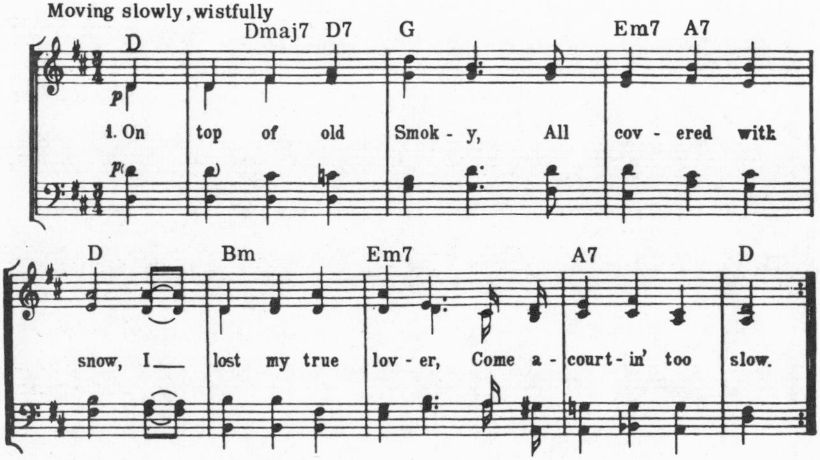
Moving slowly, wistfully
D
Dmaj7 D7
G
Em7 A7
1. On top of old Smok - y, All cov - ered with
D
Bm
Em7
A7
D
snow, I_ lost my true lov - er, Come a - court - in' too slow.

2. A-courtin's a pleasure,
A-flirtin's a grief,
A false-hearted lover
Is worse than a thief.

3. For a thief, he will rob you
And take what you have,
But a false-hearted lover
Will send you to your grave.

4. She'll hug you and kiss you
And tell you more lies
Than the cross-ties on the railroad
Or the stars in the skies.

5. (Same as 1.)

whatisthis?

it works where nothing else will.

57 ROCK-A-MY SOUL

Traditional Negro Spiritual

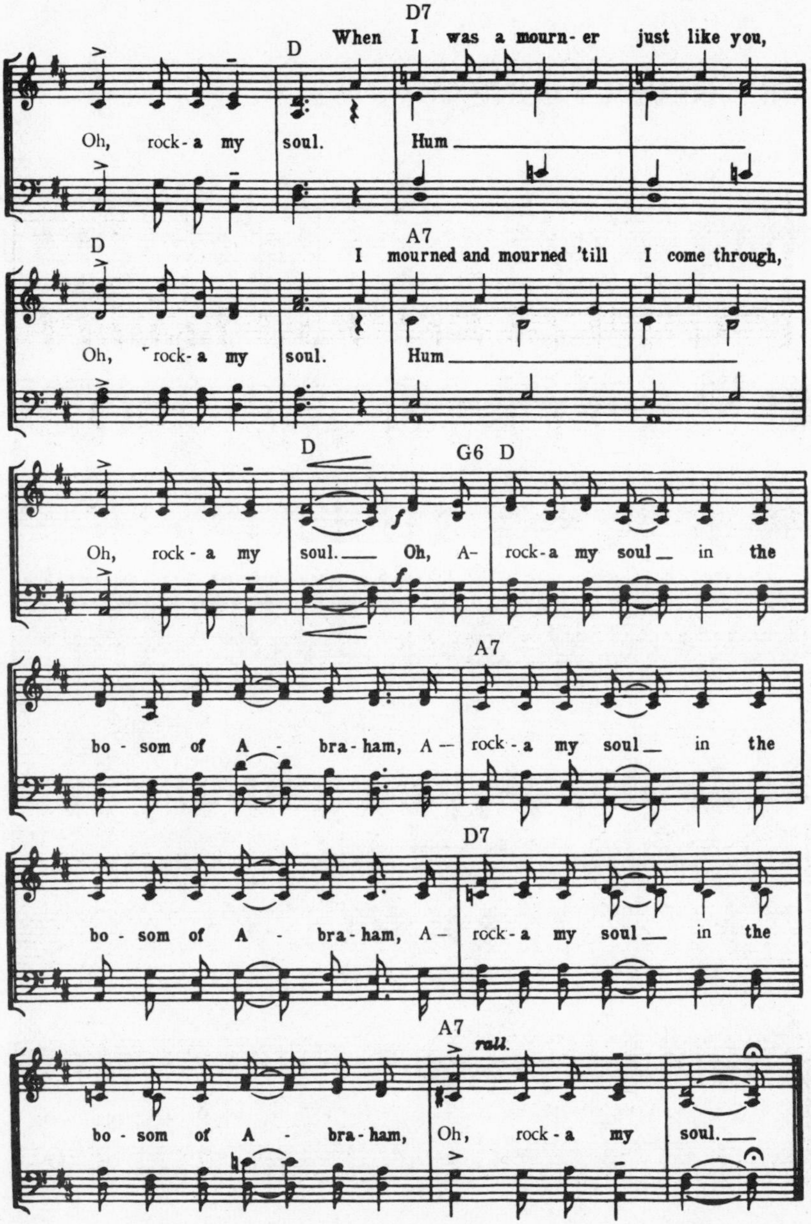
D7
When I was a mourn- er just like you,
D
Oh, rock-a my soul. Hum
D
A7
I mourned and mourned 'till I come through,
Oh, rock-a my soul. Hum
D
G6 D
Oh, rock-a my soul. Oh, A- rock-a my soul in the
A7
bo-som of A - bra-ham, A- rock-a my soul in the
D7
bo-som of A - bra-ham, A- rock-a my soul in the
A7
rall.
bo-som of A - bra-ham, Oh, rock-a my soul.

It's great

Never sleeps.

58 NEVER ALONE

E. C. H. E. C. Heidelberg

1. I nev - er wor - ry, for why should I wor - ry, Tho' sor-rows may
2. Lord, I would serve Thee, would hon - or and serve Thee In all that I
come my way? I've Some-one to hide me, to com-fort and
do or say, My heart bows be - fore Thee, I love and a -
guide me, to watch o - ver me day by day.
dore Thee, I'll live for Thee day aft - er day.
CHORUS
Nev-er a-lone, be-cause I
know my Lord is with me, Nev-er a - lone, He's al-ways stand - ing

by;
Je - sus has prom-ised to take my hand and
lead me, Nev-er a - lone, no, nev-er a - lone am I.

Never quits.

never quits.

every second

59 I HAVE CHRIST IN MY HEART

W. P. L. — Wendell P. Loveless

Martial tempo
What though wars may come, with march-ing feet and beat of the drum, For
I have Christ in my heart; What though na-tions rage, as
my heart
we ap-proach the end of the age, For I have Christ in my
heart; God is still on the throne, Al-might-y God is He;

And He cares for His own through all e - ter - ni - ty, So let
come what may, what - ev - er it is, I on - ly say That
I have Christ in my heart, I have Christ in my heart.
in my heart,

day hour month

you are there!

60 GO TELL IT ON THE MOUNTAIN

Traditional

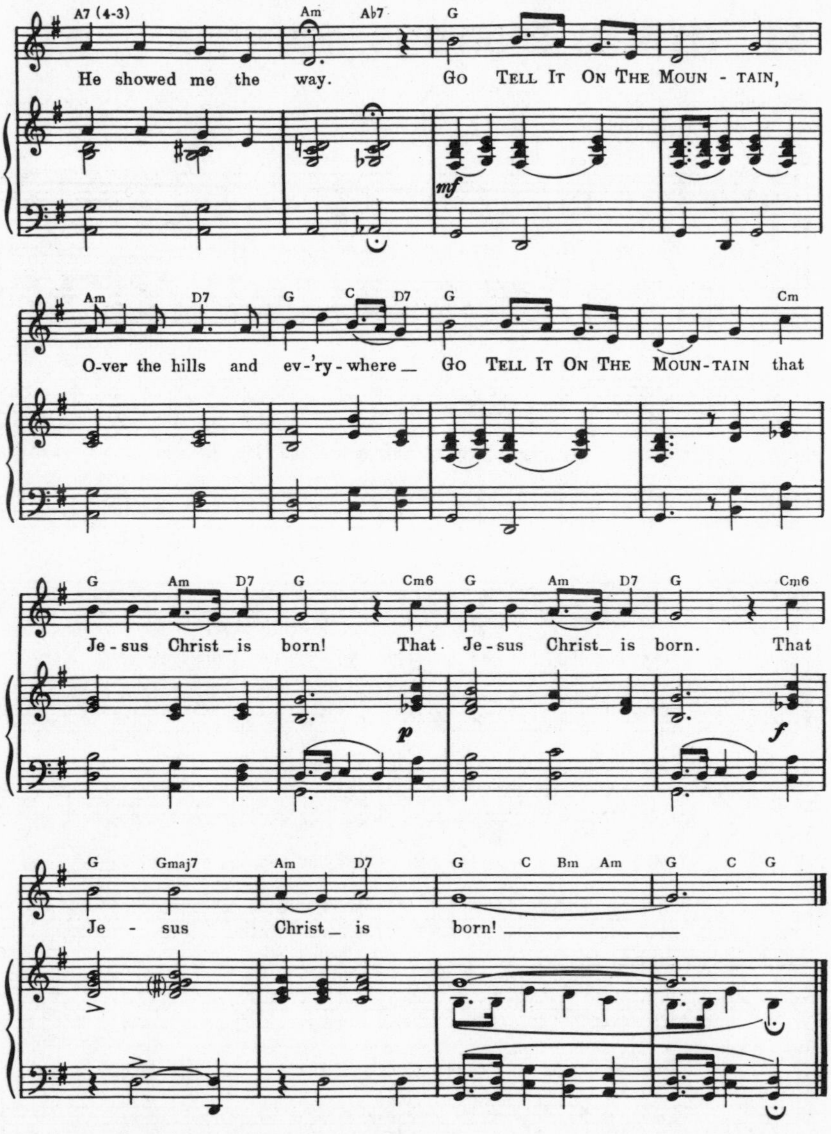
A7 (4-3) Am Ab7 G
He showed me the way. Go Tell It On The Moun - tain,
mf
Am D7 G C D7 G Cm
O-ver the hills and ev-'ry-where _ Go Tell It On The Moun-tain that
G Am D7 G Cm6 G Am D7 G Cm6
Je-sus Christ_ is born! That Je-sus Christ_ is born. That
p
f
G Gmaj7 Am D7 G C Bm Am G C G
Je - sus Christ_ is born! _______________

quiet

And service
that's
second
to none.

61 HE'S MY FRIEND

J. O. Jim Owens

Brightly (in one to a bar)
Full Chorus in Unison
I'm so hap-py to know that He's my friend
My heart sings with the joy of His love and
fav - or, Lead - ing, giv-ing me life that has no
end Je - sus, kind and com-pas-sion-ate Lord and
Parts: (S. A. T. B.)
Sav - ior, He sees my sad - ness, He knows my

fears ___ With joy and glad - ness my heart He
cheers. He is guid - ing, Keep-ing me 'til my jour - ney's
no ritard
*)
end. And I love Him, He's my friend. ___
pp

*) Cue size notes for optional ending

At last!

HELP IS HERE

Splendid news!

62 THERE IS A BALM IN GILEAD

Traditional

INTRODUCTION
There is a Balm in Gil - e - ad To make the wound-ed whole;
There is a Balm in Gil - e - ad To heal a sin - sick soul.
1. Some-times you feel dis - cour - aged, And you think your work's in vain,
2. If you can - not preach like Pe - ter, If you can - not pray like Paul,
And then the Ho - ly Spir - it Re - vives your soul a - gain.
You can tell the love of Je - sus, And say, "He died for all."

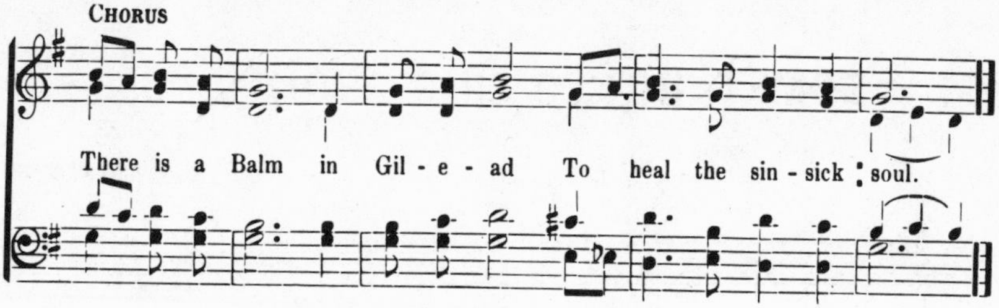
CHORUS
There is a Balm in Gil - e - ad To heal the sin - sick soul.

63 MY HOPE IS IN THE LORD

N. J. C. Norman J. Clayton

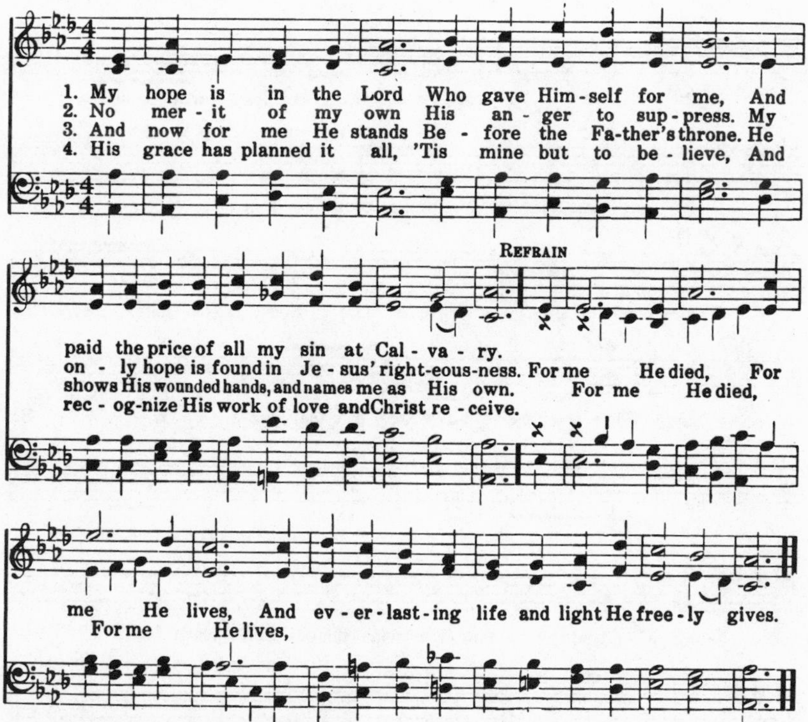
1. My hope is in the Lord Who gave Him-self for me, And
2. No mer - it of my own His an - ger to sup - press. My
3. And now for me He stands Be - fore the Fa-ther's throne. He
4. His grace has planned it all, 'Tis mine but to be - lieve, And
paid the price of all my sin at Cal - va - ry.
on - ly hope is found in Je - sus' right-eous-ness.
shows His wounded hands, and names me as His own.
rec - og-nize His work of love and Christ re - ceive.
REFRAIN
For me He died, For me He died,
me He lives, And ev - er - last - ing life and light He free - ly gives.
For me He lives,

The one who doesn't may be up a tree.

opening a present.
It's like

64 SOMETHING TO SING ABOUT

S. S. Sonny Salsbury

E A7
I've got some-thing to sing a - bout! I've got some-thing worth
E
shout-ing out! I've got some-thing that makes each day a
F#m B7 E
spe - cial day, Hear what I say. It's not some - thing that
A7
you can see, Ex - cept by the chang-es it's mak-ing in me.
E A7 E B7 3 E A7 E7
I've got some-thing to sing a - bout, how 'bout you?
A7 E
Some peo - ple sing 'cuz they're in love; Some peo-ple sing 'cuz they're free.
A7 B A
Some peo-ple sing an - y song that they hear on K.- F. - W. - B.
G B7 E
(K. - F. - W. - B.)
I've got some-thing to
A7
sing a - bout! I've got some - thing worth shout - ing out!
E A7 E B7 3 E A7 E
I've got some-thing to sing a - bout, how 'bout you?

65 OH HAPPY DAY

Traditional

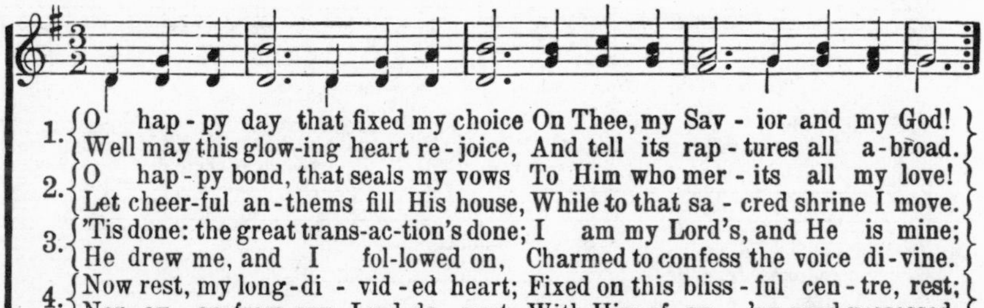
1. O hap-py day that fixed my choice On Thee, my Sav-ior and my God!
Well may this glow-ing heart re-joice, And tell its rap-tures all a-broad.
2. O hap-py bond, that seals my vows To Him who mer-its all my love!
Let cheer-ful an-thems fill His house, While to that sa-cred shrine I move.
3. 'Tis done: the great trans-ac-tion's done; I am my Lord's, and He is mine;
He drew me, and I fol-lowed on, Charmed to confess the voice di-vine.
4. Now rest, my long-di-vid-ed heart; Fixed on this bliss-ful cen-tre, rest;
Nor ev-er from my Lord de-part, With Him of ev-'ry good possessed.
FINE
Hap-py day, hap-py day, When Je-sus washed my sins a-way!
D. S.
He taught me how to watch and pray, And live re-joic-ing ev-'ry day;

Make It!

66 DOXOLOGY
(Praise God From Whom All Blessings Flow)

Bishop Thomas Ken
Clark Evan

67 GOD IS SO GOOD

Unknown

African Christian
Folk Song

D A D
God is so good, God is so good,
mf
D D7 G D A7 D
God is so good, He's so good to — me.

The best there is.

INDEX